LONG SHADOWS

Glenn Spiers

Matador
9 Priory Business Park,
Wistow Road, Kibworth Beauchamp,
Leicestershire. LE8 0RX
Tel: 0116 279 2299
Email: books@troubador.co.uk
Web: www.troubador.co.uk/matador
Twitter: @matadorbooks

ISBN 978 1789013 146

British Library Cataloguing in Publication Data.
A catalogue record for this book is available from the British Library.

Printed and bound in Great Britain by 4edge Limited
Typeset in 11pt Minion Pro by Troubador Publishing Ltd, Leicester, UK

Matador is an imprint of Troubador Publishing Ltd

I dedicate this book to my families, in thanks for their guiding hands through the dark times, and for their love and friendship during the good times.

I would like to thank Barbara, Franceska and Pam for their reading, and for their helpful suggestions.

With best wishes

23rd June
2018.

At the day's end
Time casts long shadows.

INTRODUCTION

The world had gone insane, for six years, and that was the 'normality' in our early upbringing. Both Pauline and I were wartime children, and it was a very different world we were living in then. It is difficult to be nostalgic for a time, not far removed from that hideous period in world history, when hundreds of thousands of men were killing each other, across the world. They weren't just 'men,' they were 'our men,' fathers; brothers; cousins, so it was all a part of us, and we were a part of 'it.'

But it isn't difficult to be nostalgic for the post-war period, because people had cast the war into oblivion, in desperate need to return to some kind of sanity. At last, a future had arrived.

It could not possibly be an easy transition, with women, in particular, having to step aside from the 'men's jobs' that they had done throughout the war. It wasn't a physical wrench as much as it was a massive mental shift. The role of women could never, surely, return to that of the prewar situation. But, thousands of men were returning to civilian life, desperately looking for work in an industrial situation that was geared to war, and was no longer needed. Women were virtually 'forced' back into a subservience that could never again be acceptable. What people know of 'the war' is dominated by the physical wounds it left on society. The damage done to the relationships between men and women, by the war and its aftermath, is unquantifiable, and yet, that damage was probably the most important, untreated 'wound' of the entire conflict. It must have been inevitable that the 'dominant male' was a part of me, because it was a part of the whole world. I am sure that I was just as 'neanderthal' as every other male of the time.

The visible scars of war were all around us, and in us; in the broken landscapes, and in the broken families. However, the spirit was recovering, much faster than we could have dared to expect. Even though we were just children, we also sensed the new dawn, and stepped out with an optimistic stride. The perverse 'normality' of the war years seemed a long way off, and when I met Pauline, although not aware of it, I'm sure that she and I were infused with the new confidence, in the new future.

I left school barely five years after the war had ended, and then, less than nine years after the armistice; filled with the spirit of adventure; just eighteen, and having cast off the shackles of 'the family' I had fulfilled a childhood ambition to join the Navy.

It was my first summer leave, and resplendent in my

new uniform, I was on my way home, when I met Pauline on the train. She was just sixteen, and we fell in love.

Cruelly separated, a year later, in 1955, we went our separate ways.

I vowed never to get married. Pauline married on 'the rebound' the following year. It was a marriage that was to last only eleven years, and had only been kept together for that long by the two children, Alex and Sarah.

My vow lasted for nearly eight years, but then in a fit of desperate loneliness, I married a barmaid. I proposed to her three days after we met, and we were married nine weeks later. My marriage to Rosemary lasted for forty nine years, when, after five years of dementia, Rosemary died on Christmas day, 2011.

Far too soon after her death, I know, I searched the internet for, and found, Pauline in May 2012. It was a tumultuous start, but we were married in April the following year.

Pauline and I were 'children' when we first met, and, it could be said that we were no different to any other pair of teenagers, declaring our 'undying love' for each other. We were expected to 'grow out of it,' but the problem is, we weren't given the chance to. If Pauline's parents had left us alone, it is possible that we would have separated naturally, but they interfered, and we parted still in love. It seems beyond belief, that after fifty seven years apart, we should come back together, and be able to rekindle that love, as strong as it had ever been.

It was a wonderful, romantic, fairytale story, and Pauline and I knew that we had to think very carefully about where we were going. We were fully aware that it could have been very easy for us to be swept along on a tide of romanticism, ignoring reality at our peril, but we became rapidly convinced that we loved each other as much as we ever did as teenagers.

Our story is about relationships; the complexity and the diversity of relationships beyond just that between Pauline and me, and Rosemary and me. Other people were very involved in what happened to us, and the more people that became involved, the more likely misunderstandings were going to occur. It is impossible to say why things happened as they did, because there were so many different influences at work, and although we were able to shed some light on events that we had been unaware of, at the time, many things will always remain hidden in the mists of time. It doesn't matter anymore, because no amount of analysis can change things, and we got back to living the life that we had, not the one that we might have had.

Pauline said that what she had been getting out of life was 'contentment.' She had been satisfied with it, because, as she said, 'it was all I was ever going to get.' Only after we had come together did she recognise what a negative concept 'contentment' was.

We revelled in telling 'our story,' and what delighted us the most was how people reacted to it when it was told to them. They always smiled, and the positive influence of the story showed in people's faces, but they didn't look at me, or at Pauline when we told them, they smiled at each other. I wrote the book, I think, above all, because the story touched the lives of so many people. An experience not shared can only be, at best, half an experience, and we shared it with anyone and everyone prepared to listen.

I am probably no different to anyone else in terms of settling for, easy, but prejudicial opinions. No, prejudice is too strong, really, more like non-thinking, or wrong-thinking than prejudice. It just never seems to cross our minds to think of 'that' love and old people in the same bracket. So many times I have seen announcements in a newspaper about the wedding of some old couple, and thought, ' how nice for them to have companionship in their twilight years,' but I became sharply aware of how dreadfully patronising I had been, in my attitude, when we came onto the receiving end of such thinking.

A friend of Pauline's, on hearing our story, said that we would have 'companionship' in our old age, and Pauline, quite abruptly, rebuked her by telling her that companionship had nothing to do with it; we had come together because we loved each other.

That incident happened on a bus, from Chelmsford to Great Baddow. When the lady boarded the bus, Pauline recognised her as a friend that she had not seen for many years. Pauline called out to her and the lady, Alison, sat in the seat behind us. I was introduced, and 'the story' was told, and that was when Alison made her comment. But when Alison made it, she wasn't really with us any more. She had drifted off into some other dimension. She was in her own life, not ours, and probably a lot of years ago.

It is a recognised feature of biography that the 'story' becomes much more about the reader than the writer.

Hearing about, or reading about, the lives of other people makes us become very introspective.

Life is a very serious and complex business, I know. It is often referred to as 'reality,' to distinguish it from the 'romantic,' the life of hopes and dreams. But 'reality' has become such a negative concept. When someone refers to 'reality,' it is usually meant to imply something harsh; grinding; dispiriting. No wonder people want to escape it, into a world of 'romance.' We tend to live in a cynical world of miserablism.

Pauline and I escaped that world, and brought the real and the romantic together, and I think that is why people reacted to our story as they did. We 'really' lived 'the dream;' we had opened doors.

CHAPTER 1

When we met again, for the first time, after fifty seven years apart, we couldn't stand each other. How a successful relationship survived beyond that first meeting is a miracle, and it took a lot of hard work, soul-searching, and mutual understanding, to get us back on track.

It shouldn't have happened that way, because from the very first contact, we had two weeks of wonderful dialogue, by phone and by email, and everything was going along exactly as I would have wished it, and, I believed, as Pauline would have wished it. But then, wholly without thinking, I sent her 'the letter!'

I have always believed that one of my greatest gifts in life is a total lack of common-sense! I know it sounds ridiculous, but it's true. It has got me into all sorts of scrapes, some of them amusing, some embarrassing, and some near disastrous, or downright dangerous, but more often than not it has opened up kaleidoscopical, and fantastical experiences that common-sense would, undoubtedly, have inhibited. I very rarely think before I act, and when I leap in, I do it with every part of my being committed to it, without looking first.

If, back in 2012, six months after Rosemary had died, I had gathered all of my friends; family members, and people I know, around me and told them that I was proposing to find a girl/woman that I was in love with as a teenager, but had not seen or heard of for fifty seven years; a girl, still seventeen years old in my mind, but in fact now in her seventies, I wonder what advice I would have got? I would certainly have been warned of all of the pit-falls of such a venture. 'Have you lost your mind?' perhaps, or, 'why, for God's sake?'

That's why I didn't tell anyone about it. I didn't want to be talked out of it. I wouldn't have been talked out of it, and people would have worried about me, and my mental state. I did ask myself why? Or to be more precise, 'where do you think you're going with this?' But I hadn't a clue, and all of the answers I gave myself were contradictory, anyway, so what was the point? I jumped in. I went ahead without the slightest legitimate reason for doing so, or any thought for the consequences.

I remember when I first told my friends that I had looked for, and found Pauline. None of them had had the slightest idea that I was looking for her, of course, and it must have been quite startling, because it was so soon after Rosemary had died, and they knew that I was still grieving.

I didn't tell many, only the closest friends, and they looked at me very dubiously, and some commented that they thought that I would have wanted to enjoy my freedom for a while, before embarking on another commitment. I think that, secretly, they thought I was making a big mistake. I saw it in their faces, even though no-one made so bold as to voice such an opinion. Cautions were proffered, but not advice. That is just as well, because I am not good at taking advice. Instructions, I am very good at. Unlike most people, I will always read instructions; listen to instructions, and take great care to do as I am told, but I feel that advice is a way of telling someone to do it as you would do it. An attempt to turn you into a conforming clone.

Maybe I was making a big mistake, but it would be my mistake. However, it was good to know that there were people in my life who were concerned for me, and did not want to see me get hurt. In my mind, it wasn't me that I was worried about. It was Pauline. I had hurt her very deeply back in 1955, and I did not want to do any more harm to her by my actions in trying to rekindle our relationship.

It has taken a lot of years, and a lot of experience to learn what emotional pain is. Pauline was a sweet, innocent, naïve child, and I hurt her very badly. Friends have said, 'but you were only a child yourself.' They may be right, but as true as that may be, I cannot convince myself that that is a good enough reason to hurt someone as much as I hurt her. I should have talked to Pauline; made some attempt to find out the truth, instead of just accepting what I had been told. But I was scared that the information I had been given was true. I was scared that she would tell me that she didn't love me. So, I sacrificed what we had to protect 'my' feelings, without giving any consideration to hers. My vanity had meant more to me than our love for each other, and I not only left her broken-hearted, I also did a lot of damage to myself. I know now how wrong it was; even worse, I knew at the time that I should have tested the contents of her mother's letter, and given Pauline the chance to explain herself.

People were quite right, really, to be concerned about what I was doing, since, I think, all of my friends and aquaintances were well aware of my impetuous nature. In so many ways, it was probably my impetuosity that had destroyed our happiness in 1955, and though the years since may have impressed upon me how wrong I was, they have not tempered my impulsiveness.

Our first contact, on the phone, came on June 9th 2012. I had found her through her brother, Richard, and written to her, and she phoned me. It was a surreal experience, hearing her voice from fifty seven years ago, and it did cause my knees to buckle enough to need to sit down. But it was to be just two weeks of phone-calls and emails before we met, face to face.

We both told certain friends, and family members, right at the beginning of the contact, and that's when we received the warning signals, which I ignored, almost to our peril.

Very quickly we established a very good relationship, during that first two weeks, but my impatience to meet her almost led us to disaster, when I went down to Chelmsford to see her. We had an exceptionally traumatic three days together; probably the most painful three days of my life.

It took some time, after that, to get things sorted out, and there was over a month of no contact at all, and I don't think, either of us, at that stage, thought there would ever be any contact again. But we did manage to find a way out of the maelstrom of my creating, and resume contact in a civilised manner, albeit, very warily, and I do not think either of us knew in which direction our emotions were taking us, and we remained very non-commital for some time, before we could see through the fog that was surrounding us.

Once we were in contact again, we settled to regular, Sunday evening phone-calls, and emails, that brought us closer and closer together. It wasn't meant to be like that. We had agreed to just cards at Christmas and birthdays, with, maybe, just a letter now and then. It was certainly meant to be very arms-length; platonic, but almost from the beginning of the new relationship, that had gone by the board. How it happened, I just can't remember, but I think it was obvious from the start that it would happen. In fact it happened so quickly that I think we were both very soon aware of the direction we were headed, though neither of us willing to admit it, even to ourselves.

Pauline asked me later if I had intended things to work out as they did. I told her that I wasn't sure, but I know that I was, at least, half lying,because I had certainly had it in mind as a possibility, and even a desirable one. I asked her if she had had any thoughts in that direction. She stated, quite emphatically, (too emphatically, I thought), that she had not had the slightest desire to move that way. However, I discovered, very soon after we came together, that it was a fib, when I saw an exchange of emails between her and her best friend. The pair of them had discussed the possibility of romance. A bit tongue-in-cheek, perhaps, but with an air of seriousness about it, because they had both wondered, why? What, they wondered, could my intentions be, in seeking Pauline out, if not to rekindle old flames.

Short time though it was since that first contact, back in June – just three months – a lot had happened. There had been some very big issues to resolve, which, in truth were not really settled for some considerable time. Any heady, romantic, summery, idealism was dashed, by the three day visit in June, and the cold dawn of winter hit us very hard because of that. It was a painful time, and it still hurts to recall it. However, we did move on, with nervous trepidation, and in September we were in regular contact – the Sunday phone-calls.

I was a study in agitated uselessness all day on Sundays, desperately trying to find something to fill my time, which was so unlike me. Pauline had said that she didn't want me to ring before nine o'clock, because Sarah usually called on Sundays too, and they were usually talking for about an hour, so the day was very long and slow-moving.

I like to be active, as is well known by all of my friends, but I just couldn't concentrate my mind to doing anything productive. My life had changed so much in just three months, and my mind was in such a turmoil. I had become obsessive; unable to find purpose in anything beyond the relationship that was developing. So many things had happened; some wonderful things, and some not so wonderful. My life had changed out of all recognition, and I felt that I had lost control of it, and it wasn't always a pleasant feeling. Of all the things that had happened there was only one certainty – they couldn't be un-happened. I tried watching television,but television bores me. I tried reading. I like reading, and I read a lot, but my mind kept drifting; drifting back fifty seven years, to nineteen fifty five, trying to make some sense of what had happened.

Why I let it happen as it did, way back then, I just couldn't fathom. Hindsight makes some effort to set things right, but it always fails because, though you can cast your mind back, it is impossible to recreate the situation as it really was. I could certainly find plenty of excuses for what I did, but excuses are not reasons. I have been a counsellor for long enough to know that there are no answers to 'why' questions, other than those that we think will suit us. But it is still human nature to ask 'why,' and at least attempt to find some reason for why we do things. Given the passage of time, I still do not know whether it was my feelings or my vanity that was hurt, when we had split in 1955? My actions following the breakup, would suggest that it was a 'man' thing – and I had to get my balls back. If that was the case, why am I reconnecting now, fifty seven years later? There we go again, another imponderable 'why?'

As I went through these thought processes, waiting for the time to pass before the phone-call, I felt like I was in one of those dreams where you try to control the direction you are going, but you can't do it. You go through pleasure, you suffer pain, but most of all you are intensely frustrated, because you don't get to where you want to be. It won't go right, and you just cannot control what is happening.

I felt the glow of intense pleasure as I relived that time, back in the 1950's, because it was a wonderful relationship, and even now I look upon it as being one of the happiest experiences of my life, but it was mingled with the intense pain of what soon became the unhappiest time of my life.

I felt so alone then, in my pain, but it was not that agony of the past that was gnawing at me on those contemplative Sundays, in 2012, but the new pain that I had created for myself with the, hideous, end of June experience.

Since 1955 my life had taken a lot of different turnings, and taken me through many different experiences.

Throughout those years I often thought about Pauline. Little incidents would bring her back to me, as I am sure happens to everyone when cameo moments will bring back pleasurable, and even bad experiences of the past. Often my thoughts were distinctly unhealthy, as I thought of her at times when I certainly should not have been thinking of her. I always felt that one day I would at least see her again; I knew that I wanted to see her again. When Pauline said that she had also often thought of me, though never expected to see me again, I was pleased, probably even flattered, but I didn't really believe her. I felt that there were plenty of reasons why she would want to lie about that. In fact I often felt that she was too prone to saying what she thought I wanted to hear, instead of what was true. Often I would challenge her on some contradiction in the things that she told me, and she always fell back on, 'it was a long time ago, I can't remember.' I did believe her when she first said it, in that first phone-call on June 9th. But what happened later in that month came back too often into my mind, and I couldn't help beating myself up over it.

This sort of thinking had tended to become a Sunday pattern, when I found myself drifting into areas that I did not want to be, and I had to shake myself out of this masochistic trend and get myself usefully occupied. Sunday mornings generally took care of themselves with routine stuff. Whereas before this time I would nearly always have something practical or creative to do with my time, I just couldn't seem to concentrate on doing anything particularly positive on phone-call day.

This became the time when I would jump on the bike and go out, aimlessly, on the road for a few hours. I had bought the bike, in the first place, to get the stress out of my life, though people thought I was crazy to take a motorbike test at the age of seventy-three. I know most of my friends and family did, even though they didn't say so. But I really think that bike stopped me going mad. It was a very hard time, back then, but if I had been caught speeding out on the road, I don't think, 'my wife has dementia,' would have been accepted as a reasonable excuse. It is ridiculous to think that, at my age, I had let such a thing as a romantic pursuit take over my life. The very thought, that a reconnection with the first, serious girlfriend I had, would completely dominate my entire existence. I was behaving like a child anticipating Christmas. Some suggested that it was because I was lonely. I am pretty sure that that wasn't the reason, because I was not lonely. I really have known loneliness in my life, and I know that this wasn't it. Anyway, Rosemary had only been dead six months, and to be guiltily honest, I was actually enjoying the freedom of being on my own. I have often considered myself to be rather misanthropic, but that's not entirely true; I just like to choose when I mix and when I don't.

And so the day dragged on.

One thing that did occupy my time was Sunday dinner. Even though I was on my own, I still had a Sunday roast. I often wondered how it was, when I prided myself on my radicalism, and my relish for change, that I was so conservative in so many ways. I think it is entirely to do with childhood and upbringing. Sunday roast was a never varying ritual at my grandmother's house. My mother was a dreadful cook, and I think roast beef and Yorkshire pudding, which is what we always had, would probably have been beyond her. It was my granny who taught me to cook, when I was very small, for which I have been eternally grateful. Although I had vehemently, consciously, cast off so much of my youth, there were parts of my life that were branded into my psyche. Habits like Sunday dinner were no problem, and actually, were pleasantly harmless. But some of the things that I couldn't shake off were painfully damaging, as I was now finding out. I was learning the truth of the Jesuit dictum of 'give me the boy…' Definitely the Sunday scars are still there. I hoped, as I sat at dinner, that I may not be dining alone for much longer.

To most, our story did read like a fantasy, and it was, for us, an absolutely soporific dream-time. Pauline was more than just the first serious girlfriend I had, we had really been very much in love, and fifty-eight years had passed since our first meeting, and here we were coming back together again.

'I was always so happy that we had lost our virginity to each other when we were together then', she had said, 'because, whatever else happened to me, in all those years, that could never be changed.'

We were told not to be so stupid. 'You're only children. You'll soon grow out of it.' We were only children, in so many ways, but we really believed that we were deeply in love. I think we were. That we came together again as we have now done, I think, is testament to that. Neither of us admitted that what we had in our new life, here in the 'now' was love, but it wouldn't be long before it happened, I was sure. That it would be her who said it first, I was determined. The abuse I had suffered back in June still left me raw, and I wasn't going to expose my feelings to another pounding.

It was in the last week in September that we began to commit ourselves, seriously, though we still didn't know, with any certainty, where we were going. The time was rapidly approaching when I would be moving to Spain.

I had decided, after the June debacle, that I wanted to go and live in Spain, and I had arranged to spend the winter there as a trial period, staying in a friend's house on the Costa Brava, for eight months, when he went back to his home in England. I was flying out on October 3rd. I planned to fly back on October 12th. to pick up my motorbike and take it out to Spain, because my car was in the garage for a lengthy repair, and it was the phone-call on Sunday 30th. that we committed to taking the relationship on further.

The phone-call was at nine o'clock, as usual, and it began in pretty much the same way as always. Her south-east of England accent still sounded strange to me, as I'm sure my Scottish accent did to her. Her voice wasn't 'TOWIE', thank heavens, but it was very different to how I had remembered it from way back. We went through the usual small talk, before drifting back into the past. That was all we had to talk about, really, because we hadn't got a present yet. We were remembering an iconic event from our teen time, and not for the first time, as we seemed to recall it every time we spoke – a walk in the park in Melton Mowbray, which ended with us making love on the river bank.

I was reliving it, vividly, when I heard her saying, somewhere in the distance, that she was looking forward to seeing me on October 14th. 'I really think we have become very close in the last few weeks, very close, don't you?' she was saying.

'Yes I do!' It was true, and I knew that this was as near as she would get to telling me that she loved me, at least for the time being, anyway. But we had to face the fact that we hadn't actually seen each other since the 'June meeting,' and our only communication had been by email and phone. What came next sent my head into a spin.

'I don't want you to be in the guest bedroom, this time. I think we should be together now.'

'You mean…'

'Yes, I think we are ready now to share my bed. Well?…
What do you think?'

This, I knew, was a massive decision on her part, and she
must have spent many long hours agonising about it. It was a
seismic shift from where she had been in June; it also drew a
line where there had been nothing but a fuzzy space before.
She had stepped over it into an ill-defined dimension.

Now I had to assess my position. It might seem obvious
that I would be delighted. Surely, this was what I had been
wanting, so what could be the problem? I wanted to be in
her bed, of course I did, but I wanted to be there because
she loved me, and that, she had not said. I asked her, 'Does
this mean that you love me?'

'Maybe, we'll just have to wait and see!'

My head really was reeling, and I wasn't in the mood
to be teased. There was a tension that I am sure she wasn't
expecting. She felt it and asked me if I was alright. I have no
recall what we talked about after that, but the conversation
did not last much longer.

I had dreamed of being in her bed; of making love
to her. I had told her once that I had 'red-blooded male
needs.' Who, in my dreams, had I been making love to?
Was it a lovely little sixteen-year old back in the 1950's, or
was it her, as she was at the age of seventy-four? I knew for
certain who it wasn't; that woman back in June.

Over a very short space of time we had become two
entirely different people. We had become so close now, but
that was over the phone! I think we both knew that we
were in love now, but only over the phone! I didn't even
know if I had that right, I just desperately hoped that she

loved me and that I had not been deluding myself. The distance between rural Fife and Chelmsford, Essex, has a built in safety factor. Commitment over that distance was vastly different to real touching, physical contact. She has to love me, surely, or she wouldn't be inviting me into her bed, would she? I asked myself.

I knew instantly that it came into my head that not only was it the wrong question, but a very bad question. I really started to feel dizzy, and nauseous when my mind flew back to June. If she did the same to me again, I didn't think I could take it. The memory of it was causing me pain as the images flashed into my mind.

After I got home from Chelmsford, on June 24th. after that bruising, I felt so desperately lonely; rejected and useless. It had taken a big effort to get my head straightened out again, and I was still weak from it. I decided that that was it. There would be no more contact. The fantasy was over. She said some time later,

'You are supposed to be the psychologist, surely you could see what I was doing?'

Ridiculously, I did know what she was doing at the time, but when you are the victim, on the receiving end of a psychological demolition, you do not join the dots, and try to think rationally. I looked forward to some sleepless nights, and agony filled days before I could think straight again, and make that leap into the dangerous unknown. Pauline had shown the strength of character to do it, I told myself, so I must recognise that if she can do it, so can I. At that moment, however, I felt that I couldn't make that move, yet. I didn't think I could share her bed.

Thinking practically was difficult. After that first phone contact on June 9th. I had become quite excitedly animated, wondering what Pauline looked like now. I had seen no photographs of her, and had no idea what she looked like until I had gone to see her, two weeks after we had first spoken on the telephone. I found myself looking at women in the supermarket, who would be around the same age as her. It wasn't a particularly pleasant exercise; all I could see were very old ladies, with no appeal whatsoever. I thought about old people's problems, and whether she had any that I would find difficult to deal with. I have never felt old, and I don't have 'old man's debilitations,' but I am just as prejudiced as young people, I think, and imagined all sorts of hideous ailments in her. You won't need to use much imagination to know what I mean. My difficult years with Rosemary came very much into my mind, and I knew that I would not be able to cope with anything like that for a very long time. I asked Pauline if she had thought the same about me, and she said that she hadn't, because she knew what I looked like, and knew very much more about me.

Since that last phone-call, suggesting that I should share her bed, my focus had shifted, and I was trying to imagine what she looked like naked. Strangely, we seem to have some idea in our heads that we don't change much; it's only other people who change. That was not just me, because Pauline had said, before we met again, that she was still slim, with the same short hair, and hadn't changed much since we had last been together. Of course she had changed, enormously, both in looks and manner, and I would not have recognised her at all if she hadn't approached me and asked, 'Glenn?' when I got off the airport bus at Chelmsford bus-station.

Being in bed with someone old wasn't going to be a new experience for me. Rosemary was seventy-nine when she died, but it would be a new experience for Pauline. She hadn't been in a relationship for over thirty years, and she must have wondered what being in bed with a seventy-six year old would be like. My life had been sexless for a long time, and I desperately hoped that my body was still as capable as my mind. Pauline had said that she hadn't really had any problems with the idea, because she thought that I looked pretty fit, and she was actually looking forward to it. I only wished that I could have said the same. If she was the same person I had seen back in June, then it would not happen.

After I had left her, back on June 24th I had left behind me someone that I never, ever, wanted to see again. The experience was still haunting me, as we were moving into a relationship. She sounded so differently on the phone, and she was very contrite, so maybe she had changed. But how can someone change physically, because I didn't even like the way she looked? I still had the photographs that I took of her. (When we did get together she insisted that I destroy them, and I genuinely believed that I had. However, I found copies of them in some obscure file on my computer, the other day). She looked so severe; so unfriendly, and everything about her screamed indifference, and 'go away, I don't want you here'.

I just kept asking myself, why did this have to happen? We were jollying along fine with emails and phone calls, but I knew, even as I questioned myself, that this was always, something that would have to be dealt with at sometime. I also knew that my hang-ups were my problems, and were, largely, down to my inability to accept the world as it is; a legacy of that accursed Catholic upbringing. I had to deal with it, because if I told her that I didn't want to be in her bed, that would be the end of it. After the soul-searching that she must have gone through before making the decision to take me into her bed, for me to say 'no,' would be humiliating beyond repair. I just could not let that happen. I knew that we would have to do a lot of talking, and I really would need to know the truth. There were so many inconsistencies in the things she had told me that I didn't know what to believe. I felt that if I could hear the truth, no matter how unpalatable, I would learn to live with it.

As the time got closer I began to relax my mind, and look forward to us being together. We talked about it often, on the phone, and both of us were getting excited. The tension was falling away, and although I still suffered some mood swings, I was ready, and began to think about the approaching love-making with pleasure.

Rosemary and I had not enjoyed a physical relationship for a long time. When we had first got married, we had enjoyed, what I would consider to be a very normal, and close relationship, especially when I returned from long periods at sea, but as we got older, our sex life diminished, and died.

Strangely, she did recover her libido when she was about two years into dementia. For a short time, she became almost insatiable. When I discovered why, I wasn't sure how to take it, but, in hindsight, it was certainly very entertaining. She had become very agitated and distressed one day, and I, very patiently, managed to elicit the reason why.

'Glenn's coming home this weekend,' she said, 'he's been at sea and I don't want him to find out about us, so please promise that you will stay away until he's gone.'

I had, apparently, had a double persona for several weeks, and I had been her husband at sea, and her lover at home. I can't remember how it was resolved. I can only presume that the 'lover' stayed away, because there was no more sex.

The night before Pauline and I came together, it was the last phone-call.

'I love you Pauline,' I said, abjectly breaking the vow I had made to myself that I would not be the first one to declare, 'and I hope to God you love me. I couldn't be hurt again, Pauline. I've committed myself now, and there's no going back for me. Please tell me you love me too.'

'We'll just have to wait and see, won't we,' she replied.

But, everything in the garden of the inside of my head was not all coming up roses. Apart from the ups and downs with Pauline, there, in the darkest recesses of my brain lurked that awful guilt.

It was only ten months since I had killed Rosemary, and here I was declaring my love for Pauline, and planning to be in her bed.

CHAPTER 2

It was coming up to Christmas, 2011, when Rosemary went into hospital, for the first time, on Saturday, December 17th. I wasn't there. The day before I had had cataract surgery in Edinburgh. For the whole of my life I had hated wearing glasses, and now I was being liberated from them, with the lenses in my eyes being replaced. The terrible irony was, that with the best eyesight I had ever had, I had to watch, what I had never wanted to see; my wife dying.

Early on the Saturday morning I had to go back to the surgery, in Edinburgh, for a routine, post-op, check. My sister had come to stay with us the previous week, when I had been to Edinburgh to get the other eye done, on Friday, December 9th. On the train home from Edinburgh, I phoned my sister to tell her what time I expected to be home, and it was then that I learned of

Rosemary's admission to Ninewells Hospital, in Dundee. She had collapsed, and gone into a coma. My poor sister was panicking a little. Being on her own, in an unfamilair place, it took her some time for her to work out what to do. I know I should have left her with more information on contacting emergency services.

By the time my sister and I got into the hospital, Rosemary had fully recovered, and was protesting, vehemently, that she wanted to go home. The doctor was not happy for her to be discharged, but was eventually convinced that it would probably be better, as, in her frame of mind, it could have been counter-productive to keep her there. Rosemary could be quite forceful. She was discharged, and off home we went.

By this time, Rosemary's dementia was very advanced; it had been five years since it was diagnosed, and her awareness of what was going on was very limited. My own comings and goings to Edinburgh, and her being cared for by my sister while I was out of the house, had unsettled her. Even seeing me with a plastic shield over my eye unsettled her. Rosemary knew who I was. Unlike many dementia sufferers she was always aware of my identity, and always related to me on some level or other, and she knew my sister, Elizabeth, but it was the interruptions in her routines that were a problem.

Rosemary had a good night's sleep, and was quite lucid when we took my sister to Edinburgh Airport, to fly back to Norfolk, on Sunday, December 18th. Driving home from Edinburgh, however, Rosemary became quite sleepy. Not long after our arrival at the house, after a snack meal, Rosemary again lapsed into a coma, and had to be readmitted to the hospital.

The following day, when I went in to visit her, Rosemary had, again, recovered consciousness, and, in spite of her protests, she was kept in. She hated being in hospital, because it was all so unfamiliar to her. Since she had nearly starved herself to death on one of her previous stays, Rosemary was kept on a strict food-intake monitor. It wasn't so much that she didn't like the food; it was more a case of not knowing what to do with it when she got it, because it wasn't given to her at a table, or by me, and she was left to her own devices, without being chivied, constantly, to eat. Also, her food was usually delivered to her by one person, and then taken away, some time later, completely untouched, by someone else, and there was no notification that she wasn't eating.

In the evening, I visited again, and she was, as before, quite lucid, and talkative, and wanted to know what was happening. I told her as much as I knew, which wasn't very much, because I hadn't been able to talk to a doctor, up to then.

Visiting Rosemary was always difficult, because she couldn't hold a conversation, and we just sat in silence, for most of the time.

In the late evening, I kissed her, and said that I would see her the following day, as I left.

'You're not leaving me here all on my own, are you?' she said.

'I'm sorry, I have to go home now. I'll see you in the morning.'

She was not happy at my leaving, and became agitated, and upset, and I felt very guilty at leaving her. It was always the same, and I never got used to it.

Those were the last words she ever spoke to me. The following morning, I received a phone-call from the ward to tell me that Rosemary was not at all well. She had difficulty breathing, because her lungs were gathering fluid. That was a common problem for Rosemary, both because of the state of her heart, and because of her diabetes. They were going to aspirate, but they thought I should be there.

When I got to the hospital, the aspiration had been done, and Rosemary was breathing normally, but she was in a very deep coma.

The consultant took me into an office to give me the prognosis, which wasn't good.

'We have done a brain scan,' he said, 'and we can see that there is considerable damage. Much more than we saw at the last scan. It looks as if she has had another, quite large, stroke. I'm afraid that it is very unlikely that she will regain consciousness.'

'Do you mean she is dying?' I asked, dejectedly.

'No. She could live for a long time, yet. She could even come out of the coma, but the damage to her brain is much too severe for any kind of normal life, now.'

'She hasn't had a 'normal life' for a long time, but she has had a life, with some enjoyment of things. If she did recover, would she be mobile? Would she be able to do things?'

'Mr Spiers, I'm sorry, but she can't recover. When I say

that she could come out of the coma, that would only be a clinical response. Her brain would not be active.'

'So, even if she comes out of the coma, she will be in a vegetative state?'

'I'm sorry. Yes. That is the case. I'm really sorry Mr. Spiers, but decisions are going to need to be made. It is not up to me to decide, or to make suggestions. I'm afraid that what happens now is entirely your decision.'

'Are you absolutely certain that she can never recover?'

'We can never be certain about anything, I'm afraid, Mr. Spiers. All I can say is that it is very, very unlikely.'

I was distraught; devastated. Even though I had known that this time would come, probably expecting it to have been much sooner than it was, it was still exceptionally difficult to accept that it had arrived.

'I have a lot of thinking to do. Could I speak to you later, please, when I have had time to absorb all this?'

'Of course you can. There is no hurry, no hurry at all. I could see you tomorrow morning, if you like.'

I slept much better than I could have hoped that night. I was exhausted, I know, more mentally than physically. The guilt had already started, because I could not help feeling relieved that the time had come. I hated myself for feeling that way, but it had been such a tough five years, and recently it had become, on occasions, almost unbearable. I knew what decision had to be made. I should have shared it. But I didn't.

When Rosemary's dementia was first diagnosed, we were surprised. Why, I will never know, because there had been clear symptoms of it for at least two years before the diagnosis. We were probably not aware, because, like most people, we thought dementia was about loss of memory. We had five difficult years to find out that it meant a lot more than that.

There had been no notification that Rosemary had been referred for a mental health check, before the appointment arrived in the post, to go to the Mental Health Assessment Centre, in Cupar. On her last visit to her GP she had told him that she was concerned about her loss of memory, but had thought no more about it. Even then we only found out what the appointment was for when we got there. Then it was the, familiar, 'do you know who the Prime Minister is?' questions. (As if anyone, demented or not, could forget Tony Blair). I sat in on the consultation, and it was obvious then that there was a problem. Rosemary laughed her way through the difficulties, with,

'God, I can never remember what day of the week it is. It's Tuesday, isn't it? No, it's Thursday. Yes, Thursday, because that's the day I......'

Unfortunately, I was prone to putting in my contribution, by making excuses for her.

'The first thing you must do is to get Power of Attorney,' was the major advice at that meeting, 'because if you don't, then if, at some time in the future, Rosemary's bank ruled that she was no longer competent to manage her own affairs, then her accounts could be frozen.'

That proved to be one of the most upsetting processes of them all. Rosemary had been told that she had vascular dementia, and that her condition could worsen quite quickly, and we should see a solicitor as soon as possible, because the Power of Attorney could only be granted when the person granting it was fully aware of what was happening. Our solicitor was also a friend, and he was deeply upset at our news, and promised to make it as painless as possible. But, when he asked Rosemary to tell him that she completely understood what she was doing, the tears came, all round, when she answered,

'Yes… I'm signing my life over to Glenn, because I'm going dottled.' (The Scots word for dementia).

The worst part of the dementia was during the first two to three years, because Rosemary knew what was happening to her, as she slowly declined, and for a long time it frightened her.

She once said, 'I've got an honours degree in English, and I can't even understand what's going on in a TV soap.'

It was so distressing to see her slipping away into another, unknown dimension, whilst at the same time being aware, herself, that it was happening.

For every person who has dementia, there must be a unique type. I learned very quickly that the memory loss was the least of the problems. It's not just a loss of memory, it's like a complete rearrangement of the 'furniture' inside the head. It was quite possible for Rosemary to hold two, diametrically opposed ideas in her head at the same time. I could be two entirely different people, there with her, and yet, not there with her. I was always away at sea, but also, always at home. She was a diabetic, too, and I cared for her and administered all of her treatment; organised her numerous tablets; gave her her injections; put cream on her sore bits, did the cooking; cleaned the house;

did the garden; changed the bed on the occasions she was incontinent, and sat with her every evening before showering her and putting her to bed. But she still claimed that I was never there, and that I didn't live there.

When speaking to her brother or sister on the phone, she would often tell them,

'Glenn's home this weekend, so I'll be able to cook something nice.'

They knew, however, that it had been too dangerous to let her anywhere near a cooker, for years.

Amazingly, she always knew who she was talking to on the phone. She never forgot who people were, she just mixed them around a little. When my sister was staying with us, at the time Rosemary was taken into hospital, Rosemary asked Elizabeth if she was my wife.

'No, you're Glenn's wife,' replied my sister.

'Yes, I know that, I'm not stupid. But you could easily be his wife as well.'

Once, when I went to visit her in hospital, the nurse said,

'We're surprised to see you. Your wife said that you wouldn't be able to visit because you are in the Navy, and at sea.'

'I'm 74 years old,' I said. 'Even the modern British Navy, with all of its cuts, is not yet that desperate.'

'Yes, we did wonder about that,' she laughed, 'we thought she might have a toy-boy.'

'That's not as unlikely as you think,' I told her. 'She does have a toy-boy, and that's me as well.'

One evening, when I went out to the freezer in the

garage, to get something for our evening meal, Rosemary locked the door, and I couldn't get back in. I had a spare key hidden outside, for emergency use, so I collected that. But I still couldn't get in because she had been crafty enough to put the 'snib' down on lock, so the key wouldn't work. I called to her at the window, and she just stood looking at me. She said that she wasn't letting me in, because I wanted to kill her! Neither of us got anything to eat that night, and I had to sleep in the car. I rang the doorbell in the morning. She let me in;

'Where have you been?' she asked me.

She couldn't understand why I just burst out laughing.

What I do find difficult to understand, is why, if dementia is supposed to be caused by dead brain cells, how is it that she could sometimes be quite lucid, and hold a reasonable conversation with someone? Everyone we knew commented on that, and often remarked that there were occasions when it was difficult to believe that she had dementia. Brain cells cannot come back to life, now and then, surely? I think it's as I said earlier, about the rearrangement of the 'furniture.' It seems as if sometimes, things briefly get back into the correct alignment.

Because of the incredible amount of medication she was on, Rosemary suffered all sorts of side-effects. She tended to get very dry skin, and one morning, when I was rubbing cream on her legs, she looked down at me, down on my knees, and said,

'You didn't sign up for this when you married me, did you. You have to do so much for me, Glenn. I'm sorry.'

It was moments like that that tore the heart out of me.

*

On December 19th, I went back into the hospital, to speak to the consultant. He was still of the same opinion as he had been previously, that Rosemary had no chance of a normal recovery. I told him that I did not want her resuscitated, if she could not have a decent quality of life. He looked, so sorrowfully, into my eyes, and he squeezed my arm.

I had agonised over it for hours. I had questioned my motives. Was I looking forward to the release? Was I taking this action for her, or for me? One thing I did know, and I will always know, is that I was giving my permission for Rosemary to be killed. It was no-one else's decision; just mine, and I can never get past that, even though everyone around me said that I had no choice.

It was tough, but I am glad that I didn't involve anyone else in the decision. I don't think it would have been right to burden other people with it. Everyone said that it was the correct decision. My son, Gordon, who had been closer than anyone to her, having spent time inside his mother at the beginning of his life; his children; his grandchildren; Rosemary's brother and sister, said it was the right decision. I know it was the right decision, but I'll never believe it.

Euthanasia is not legal in Scotland. You are not allowed to kill a person by administering any substance into the body. You are, however allowed to kill someone by *not* administering substances into the body that are required in order to keep that person alive.

You are not allowed to kill a person by giving, to eat or drink, anything that would endanger life. You are, however, allowed to kill someone by denying that person the sustenance that is essential to life.

Rosemary was in a single room, on her own. When I went back in to see her in the evening, and to move into the room to stay with her, the 'death sentence' was posted on the door of the room.

'Cease all medication. Nil by mouth.'

It seemed so stark, and it made me feel my guilt intensely.

On December 20th, Gordon, and his partner, Lili, came up from London, and moved into the room with me. We slept in an armchair, in turns, and we slept on the floor, for the time it took until Rosemary died. Being Christmas, the hospital was quiet, and we were allowed to have our meals in the staff canteen.

Rosemary remained in a coma, and looked very peaceful. She did not show any signs of distress at all. All three of us spoke to her, constantly, but there was never any response, and I let her brother and her sister speak to her, on the phone, but there was no indication that she was aware of what was happening, as she showed no response of any kind. Peter and Margaret were pleased, though, because they felt that she may have been aware of them in her deep subconscious.

On Christmas day, Gordon wanted to go and visit his grandchildren, in Glenrothes, a couple of hours drive away, to be with them for Christmas day, and to share the joy of their Christmas with them, so he and Lili left me alone with Rosemary.

It was about four o'clock in the afternoon that the clear signs of the impending end showed themselves, so I went and got the nurse. Two nurses returned to the room with me. I took Rosemary in my arms and I spoke to her, as one of the nurses held my arm. The other one was crying, and she left the room.

At 4.15, Rosemary's eyes opened wide; she looked wide-eyed into my face, and with a slight twist of her mouth, she gave out one deep last sigh, and she was still; her eyes closed again.

I laid her head back on the pillow. The nurses left me alone with her, and I cried for a long time, and then I phoned Gordon.

As I waited for Gordon and Lili to arrive, I sat and stared, aimlessly, out of the window, and, like the myth of the drowning man, my life passed before me. I remembered how our marriage, back in 1963, had faced its first test, as I received a draft, a week before the wedding. When I phoned my prospective new boss, an ophthalmic consultant, to tell him of my arrangements, he, very kindly, told me that he could manage to look after himself for a couple of weeks.

We were allowed to have a week's honeymoon before I left for the new job, as an optician, in the south of England, and it was about three months before Rosemary was able to join me.

When she was very pregnant with Gordon, Rosemary went into hospital in Aberdeen for several weeks before he was born, because of her serious heart condition. (We had been advised not to have children). I was on a ship, then, and by sheer luck, I was able to get one night's leave on the night that Gordon was born. In the morning I held him in my arms. I kissed him; I kissed Rosemary, and I said goodbye. Gordon was ten months old when I next saw them.

I was in Borneo. It was no life for a married man, and certainly no life for his wife. I bought myself out of the Navy, to go to university in Aberdeen, and to plunge us into five years of penury, during my student days. I was teaching when Rosemary went to university. One year teaching together in the same school, in Stonehaven, and I uprooted us again, when I became a politician, and we moved to teaching jobs in Fife, to be near my prospective constituency.

Admittedly, Rosemary was behind me, every step of the way, but it was the stoicism with which she stood up to the rigours of the life that I subjected her to that deserve enormous admiration. We taught out our careers together in the same school in Kirkcaldy. More years of financial hardship, as every penny we had went on my political career, which, eventually, came to nought.

In 1993, Rosemary had the heart operation, that gave her a new lease of life, but which also sowed the seeds for the dementia that eventually killed her.

As my mind went through that saga, of our lives together, I marvelled at the fact that our relationship had survived at all, as I remembered the times I had put our marriage under terrible strain; the times when Rosemary should have left me, but she didn't. She had led me forward from the front, or she had pushed me on from behind.

More than anything, Rosemary's loyalty had gone beyond what any reasonable man could have expected.

By the time Gordon and Lili returned, I had lived again through forty nine years of marriage. We packed our sleeping bags, and other belongings, into bin bags, and left. Hospitals are always too hot for me, and leaving that little room was like leaving the womb, and emerging into the cold of the world; a new life to begin.

I shivered my way to my car, which had been sitting in the cold car park for five days; flung the bin bag into the boot, and drove away, hoping against hope, that I would never see the inside of Ninewells hospital ever again.

It was just six months later, and I was in contact with Pauline. It was too soon; far too soon, I know. Rosemary's sister, Margaret, was not at all happy, when I broke the news about Pauline, in October.

'Rosemary hasn't been dead ten months yet, and you're already in another relationship, and with someone you already knew. Rosemary was my sister, and I loved her very much, and I just cannot understand why you are doing this. It just doesn't seem right.'

I could not dispute what Margaret was saying, and I had felt guilty, and beaten myself up over it, from the beginning. I had managed to keep my guilt close, but now it was going to hurt. I had coped because Rosemary had said, many times, that she knew that I would outlast her, and she wanted me to find happiness with someone else after she was gone. I reciprocated, but always dismissed what she said at the time, as nonsense, but her health had always been bad, and I knew that what she said was probably true.

The last five years of her life, as I nursed her through those dreadful times, I had had to face the fact that we were approaching the end, and I had to think about how I was going to face life without her. I did not, however, think that I would be getting married again, not at the age of seventy four. Pauline was nowhere in my thoughts at that time.

CHAPTER 3

When I look back over our early history, it is quite remarkable how much Pauline and I had in common, in terms of what shaped our personalities, and our relationship with our world. Our early experiences of school, for instance, were very similar.

Not many of my aquaintances are aware that I was not born in Scotland, and that I am only Scottish by choice rather than by birth or descendence, and that my given name isn't actually Glenn. I was never Christened Glenn, and even now any mail I receive from official government departments is addressed to 'Anthony Spiers,' in spite of me telling them that Glenn has been added to my name. (You can't change your name without a Deed Poll, but you can add names). I was given the name 'Glenn' as a nickname by a friend that I had made at Victoria Barracks, in Portsmouth, when I first went into the Navy. That is the 'Navy' that I was never going to get into, according to my mother, because I had been at death's door since I was born. Throughout the fifties, up until the time I left home for the sea, I was known by all as Tony.

My mother was a raving hypochondriac, who, when she ran out of things to be dying from, decided to live her sickly life vicariously through me. I had slight asthma, which I do not have at all now. This, according to my mother, would necessitate spending most of my miserable life in an iron lung, inches away from death. I think I grew up believing that everyone spent life smelling of camphorated oil and goose grease, and wearing thick knitted underwear. I remember, with utter horror, the times sitting in doctors' surgeries with the sweat dripping off my nose, under layers of clothing and scarves, while my mother explained to everyone in earshot that I 'had to be kept wrapped up'.

She was not a 'cuddling' person, my mother. I cannot remember, ever, getting a hug from her, or seeing my sister get a hug, either. I am the exact opposite; I'm a 'spontaneous hugger.' In my world I see hugging as being as natural and as necessary as smiling.

I did grow up, however, with perfect manners, and impeccable social etiquette. I was taught to raise my hat, and say 'how do you do,' to strangers; to 'be seen and not heard.' We were taught the correct way to use our cutlery; 'always move the soup spoon away from you, not towards you.' I am even grateful that I could always feel comfortable in any company, anywhere. Unfortunately, well-mannered as I was, I hadn't even a modicum of social skills. I had the manners to mix with people, but no ability to relate to them.

I loathed the mollycoddling, but I was so conditioned to it that I used to tell pals, whenever our games got boisterous, that I couldn't join in because I might drop dead. But as I got older I started to rebel, and even run about occasionally. A cough or a sneeze or two, and a sick-note was sent to the school, explaining my three week absence as 'another one of his attacks'. I was given daily notes to give to my teachers asking for me to be excused from just about anything that involved breathing. I think I must have been the only kid in school who tore up my excuse notes, instead of forging them to avoid doing things.

The primary school I attended was an old Victorian village school in Leicestershire, of austere red sandstone, with teachers to match. I hated it there, and desperately longed to get away, which probably influenced my mother's, later decision, to move both my sister and me to a Catholic school in the City of Leicester. We didn't need to move because that village school was a straight through school, from infant to leaving at fifteen. So I must take the blame, in some ways, for what happened to us.

At the primary school I was bullied, unmercifully by both teachers and kids, for being so pathetic. If I had been one of them, I would have bullied me. 'Bugger off and wheeze over someone else four-eyes,' I was once told, when I tried to make friends with a boy in one of my classes. I gravitated towards the other pathetic kids, but even they found me too much to put up with. At the primary school they didn't have a 'holy group,' or, I've no doubt I would have sought solace in among them, as bullied kids tend to do. PE classes were an absolute purgatory. In the changing room I would become the centre of attention. 'Come and look at this poor sod, he's got two pairs of pants on and three vests!'

Of all the miseries of childhood that I went through, those terrible years were what I desperately looked forward to getting away from, and that, I felt, I could never forgive my mother for. At least when I went to secondary school I left that behind, but sadly I was to discover that any education I did receive was probably at that village primary school, and learning was left behind too.

The Catholic school was dreadful. I cannot remember learning anything other than kneeling and praying, although I did learn to smoke, which was almost a compulsory part of the 'lunch-time curriculum,' but I can remember, vividly, most of the teachers I had, and I do remember, fondly, the woodwork classes, because I have always loved doing practical things. Every aspect of the curriculum was dominated by 'the Faith'. Unfortunately, it absorbed me, and frightened me. I was in perpetual fear that I would die and go to Hell.

I think my mother had ambitions for me to become a priest, so on top of the indignities of dying, and desperately trying to survive the brickbats of this life, I had to survive the next one too, by rushing off to Confession regularly to ask forgiveness for the terrible crimes of tearing up sick-notes, having lewd thoughts about Bridget O'Reilly, and masturbating. Or the most heinous crime of all, comparable only to murder – missing Mass on Sunday; a Mortal Sin that would have sent me straight to Hell, if I'd died on the way to confession instead of on the way home, without even the privilege of spending a couple of million years in Purgatory to do penance for the monstrous crimes committed during my few short years of life.

When the Bishop paid a visit to the school, I rushed to be the first in line to get down on one knee to kiss his signet ring, which meant that if I died right there and then I would go straight to heaven. I would not have to 'pass go' or 'collect two hundred pounds'. All this I believed. (Later in life, when I entered politics, and stood for parliament, in a mining constituency, and what was then the constituency with the largest electorate in Scotland, I was attacked by the NUM Scotland for having been educated at 'a fancy English school!').

I left secondary school, at the age of fifteen, in exactly the same position as every other pupil who ever went to that school, without a single qualification to my name.

Our mother was a devout Catholic, who never went to Mass, 'not with my back'. My sister and I, however, were never allowed to miss going off to the church every Sunday morning. I say going off to the church, because that is what we did, but the church was about three miles from our home, and we, sometimes, got diverted, unintentionally of course, to the swings in the park. (Something else to rush off to confess). This often proved difficult for us because neither of us had any way of telling the time, so it necessitated asking other people in the park what the time was so that we didn't over or under stay our liberty, and arouse suspicion when we got home. Strangely, we felt most guilt about the sixpence we had been given for the collection, because we didn't really know what to do with it. I cannot remember at all how we did overcome that particular difficulty.

That I was growing up psychologically warped would be an understatement, (but then perhaps that could be said of all children). There were other influences though, that did have a great effect on my later life, apart from religion. It was during my childhood that my attitude to women was being nurtured, though I wasn't aware of it at the time.

My early childhood, at primary school was spent enjoying 'The War'. It sounds strange to say 'enjoying' I know, but there was a lot to enjoy during 'The War', for a boy. It was adventurous and exciting. We spent endless playtimes racing around playgrounds, arms outstretched, engines roaring, in our spitfires, machine-gunning other, enemy, planes out of the sky. Unfortunately I was usually forced to play a German, and get killed pretty quickly, and with a grissly end, which normally involved suffering real wounds, so much of my 'flying' was on solo sorties, behind enemy lines.

In and out of school we let our imaginations run wild, with tales of how many 'Japs' our dads had killed with their bare hands. We went to fantastic war zones and fought heroic battles. The news was listened to avidly, every night on the radio – there were special war broadcasts – so that we would be up to date with the next day's games. There were even real fantastic events to witness, as we sat gazing out of our bedroom window, watching bombing raids over Leicester. The night Coventry was bombed was witnessed by us, even from our house in the Leicestershire countryside. We couldn't hear anything, but the night sky was lit up so brightly that it could be seen from huge distances. Lord Haw Haw had even telegraphed the event.

It was the backdrop to many heroic feats the following day in the playground. There was an airfield not far from our house at a place called Desford, and we watched numerous Lancaster and Wellington bombers taking off in squadrons, and we saw fewer coming back, and many times, crippled stragglers, limping home with stilled propellers on one or two of their four engines. I remember one that didn't make it home and crashed in a field two or three hundred yards from our house. It crashed in flames, and live ammunition seemed to be firing off for ages, which kept the RAF fire engines at bay, unable to do anything until the bullets stopped firing. It had no bombs on board, thank God. Souvenir-hunters came flocking from Leicester the following day, to be sent packing by the RAF police, but after the excitement had all died down, and the wreckage cleared, kids from all around went into the field, and we were able to pick up bits of burned aluminium pieces, and I can still remember the smell of burning aircraft that hung over the area for days. I know that some boys got small instruments, and even live bullets, which became prize 'swap' currency for ages. But our dads, uncles, and older brothers were 'away', and 'the mice' were out to play.

I was only a child, but I knew that there were things going on that shouldn't be happening. It was always seen when a finger went up to a mouth in a 'shush,' and we were pointed at, though we were always considered too young to understand, and everyone must be familiar with, 'not in front of the children'. Parents did not seem to comprehend that we were young, not morons.

A boy in my class once asked me if it was true that my mother went with 'Yanks'. We did have visitors to the house, and I remembered Jimmy and Johnny and Len, though Len was RAF, not a 'Yank'. I had never thought much about it, because whenever they were there it meant chocolate and chewing gum, and stuff.

The impression of one situation is so strong that I can remember, vividly, the day when the deputy head came and took me out of the class, in front of a hushed teacher, who cast her eyes to the floor. Being taken out of class usually meant only one thing, but the deputy head was smiling, so it couldn't be that. My sister was already in the deputy's room, as the deputy told us that our dad had come home on leave, and as it was just for one day we were to be allowed to go home, because he was going to take us to the pictures. Our excited rush home was dashed when we discovered that our 'dad' was Len. He did take us to the pictures. Ridiculously, I remember that the picture we saw was called 'Doctor Cyclops ', about a one-eyed mad scientist, who shrank people with a ray-machine, and little people, wrapped in pocket hankies, ran around throughout the film trying to escape.

'NO,' I snapped, 'My mother doesn't go with Yanks.'

This early education into womankind was going on all around us, and even in our small village, (there was an American base quite close by), we saw used condoms hanging in lane-side hedges. I've no idea how we knew what they were, but we did, and the boys had a particularly foul name for them. I think everyone knew of at least one soldier who came home to an unexpectedly enlarged family. The folk wisdom excused it as 'the war!'

When the war ended I was almost ten, and my father came home. We had barely seen him throughout the war, so we knew very little of him, and we didn't relate to him at all. In fact, we never got to know him for very long before he disappeared with a peroxide blonde called Phyllis. It must have been love because they were together, apparently, for the rest of their lives, or until one died – I've no idea which of them went first. My sister and I were never allowed to see him or communicate with him, ever, because he was 'just a bad lot'.

Those wartime memories, and many other experiences I have had during my life have made it very difficult for me to place a complete trust in women, even to this day, and Pauline's betrayal in 1955, was just confirmation of my mistrust.

For no reason that I can think of, I had always, from a very young age, wanted to go into the Navy, and following two, ridiculously wasted years, as an apprentice television technician, (from which I was eventually sacked), and a short time working in the Imperial Typewriters factory in Leicester, drilling holes in things, (truly inspiring!), I joined the Royal Navy, and reported for training in January 1954.

My mother had known of my ambitions, and had constantly put me down with, 'they'll not have you; not with your chest,' so when I arrived home from Derby, after having passed my medical, she was dumfounded, and vowed to write to the Admiralty to put them right. I have to say that I had gone there with the greatest of trepidation, and was as amazed as she was when I passed.

There are all sorts of reasons why people do what they do, and sometimes we could spend a lifetime trying to account for why people make certain decisions. (As a Historian, I have always kept this in mind), and having gone into the wholly wrong job entirely because a friend of mine had gone that way. I did it again when I went into the Navy. (Although, as it turned out, it was not the wrong choice that time. It was a wonderful career, and one that I never regretted, even for a moment). When I was asked at the recruiting office why I wanted to join the medical branch, I said that it was because my mother had been a nurse. I did not think they would be impressed if I had told them the truth; that a bloke I had worked with had been a 'sick-bay tiffy' before he was invalided out, and he told me that it was a 'pretty good number'.

There were two seriously pet hates in my life that had developed in early childhood. The first was hospitals. I had spent so much time in them as a child that I shuddered every time I walked past one, or heard one mentioned. My second hate was schools, for obvious reasons, since I had left school, following my 'education' without a single qualification, and I was amazed that I could even read and write, since I could not remember having learned to at school. You probably think it strange, therefore, that I joined the medical branch in the Navy, and even stranger that on leaving the Navy twelve years later I went to University, and then on to become a teacher.

*

All I can tell you about Pauline's life, before me, was what she told me, so I have very little detail. As I have said earlier, her name was Pauline Mary Phizacklea, and she was always known as Mary at home, and by everyone else as Pauline. It was Pauline that she introduced herself to me as, but all surviving members of her family still know her as Mary, which can still be a bit confusing, as several guests discovered at our wedding. I knew that she had one brother, Richard, but I did not know of Dorothy, her older sister, or her youngest brother, Donald, who, although ten years her junior, was the one she was closest to, and always went to in times of trouble. Sadly, Donald, at the age of seven, was too young to be of any help to her, when I caused her problems.

She told me that she had only one ambition, and that was 'to go home'. She was born in Hawton, near Tamworth, on May 22nd 1938, into a farming family. Well, her father was the farmer. When she was just three the family picked up the milking pail and the mucking-out shovel and moved to another farm at Laxfield, in Suffolk. (They had a habit of moving on, and did it quite a lot, as I was to discover).

Pauline said that she didn't settle well in the local school in Suffolk, and she didn't like it, for the short while that she was there, before her family 'disposed' of her for

44

the first, of several times that they got rid of her. It couldn't have been too bad, though, because she said that she made a lot of friends, locally, that she missed when she and her older sister, Dorothy, were shipped off to a Catholic boarding-school, when Pauline was eight years old.

It was a Dominican Convent at a place called Brewood, (pronounced brood) near Wolverhampton.

That was her first isolation from the family, but not the only time, as she was constantly exiled throughout her young life, and spent very little time at home. The Convent was to be Pauline's whole educational, and life experience until she left school at fifteen. It was not a pleasant experience for her, and she disliked it intensely, for several reasons. As soon as they got there she felt out of place. As the daughters of a struggling farmer, with a local accent from Suffolk, they thought they were looked down on by the unwelcoming, predominantly posh daughters from wealthy homes. Unlike me, Pauline was not intimidated into the 'Faith'. Quite the contrary, she questioned it, constantly, and was branded 'rebellious'. If she had known what it meant, at that time, she would probably have described herself as an Atheist.

As far as I can gather she did receive a better education than I did, but not much better, as she left school with exactly the same number of qualifications as me. She said that as far as she could remember, she knew of only two girls who left with the School Certificate.

When she was about ten, she, Dorothy and a friend were involved in, what now can be seen as a funny incident, but not so at the time, when the three of them attempted an escape. They hadn't actually made civilian clothes out of old army blankets, and, in fact just walked out of the school, and made it, undetected, to Wolverhampton railway station. The plan was to get platform tickets, which cost a penny, (in those days you needed one to get onto the platform to do your 'Brief Encounter' farewells), and then to sneak onto a train to London, and then a train for home. Unfortunately, the plot was foiled when they were swooped upon by nuns who took them into custody, and returned them, under escort, back to 'camp.' The taxi fares were taken out of their pocket-money allowance from home.

Most of her young life, Pauline felt, was spent in the shadow of Dorothy. Her time at the Convent, Pauline believed, had been, initially, to provide company for Dorothy. Everyone in the family, and even at school, would fall over themselves to please Dorothy, she thought, and this is certainly something that has been confirmed by all the other members of Pauline's family that I have spoken with. I never met Dorothy; she died before Pauline and I were back together, but Pauline told me that Dorothy was prettier, more lively and more vivacious than her, and was the centre of attention wherever she went. Pauline, even in her seventies, really believed this; she had grown up, so brain-washed into that idea, that her confidence in herself was so low. Pauline was a beautiful schoolgirl, (I have photographs), and a beautiful woman, and the more I learned of Pauline's young life the more I related to her, on so many levels.

After leaving school Pauline made a very brief visit home before being shipped off to Southend to stay with an aunt and uncle, and their daughters. She has no idea why that happened. Her family had moved from Suffolk to Melton Mowbray by then. Pauline was allowed another flying visit home before, next, being packed off to a pre-nursing college in Bath, Somerset, for a two year course.

Her parents were strangers to her, and it cannot be any wonder that her life's ambition was to go home. The feeling remained with her, always. She described herself as a 'home-bird', and even on holidays, after around ten days she would begin to get restless, and long for her garden, and homely domesticity. This need eventually overwhelmed her. She was sent to Bath in January 1954. By the summer she had had enough; phoned her parents and told them she was on her way home.

Pauline boarded the train at Bath station, and was on her way. She was in a dream state, looking forward so much to getting home, and remembers little of the start of the journey. She thinks that she had to change trains at some junction or other that she just cannot remember the name of, before eventually boarding the train for Leicester. Although she had no idea it was coming, she was heading for far more than Leicester and Melton Mowbray that day.

CHAPTER 4

Before I left school I had made some efforts to de-wimp myself. I joined the sea cadets, and I even took up boxing, very unsuccessfully, but I still had a long way to go before I had the confidence to make some real progress in life.

My induction into the Royal Navy began at Victoria Barracks, Portsmouth, in February 1954, just after my eighteenth birthday. With my small case packed, I caught the bus from Scraptoft into Leicester, and walked to the railway station. My mother was working, so wasn't able to see me off. I learned later that my grandfather had set out on his bike for the four mile journey to the station to see me off, but had got his bike wheel stuck in a tramline, fallen off his bike, and buckled a wheel, so he didn't make it. It was a nice thought, though, and I appreciated it. I think my mother heaved a sigh of relief when I went, because I hadn't been the best of sons before I left home.

Victoria Barracks was a daunting place. It was big, and for the first time I was to experience 'mess' living, in a large dormitory shared with a lot of other men, and with a bedside locker for everything I owned, and with no privacy. It was to be like this for a lot of years, and it was surprising how quickly we adjusted to it.

We were turfed out of bed at the crack of dawn, with a lot of shouting and banging of dustbin lids, and friendly obscenities. Quick ablutions, then ushered into the massive dining hall for a hurried breakfast, before rushing back to the mess to change, rapidly, into boots, and other marching gear. This was to be six weeks basic training; everything done at the double, and endless marching. I think we got to know every inch of that huge parade ground. Our shoulders ached from carrying a rifle, and doing rifle drill. We were shouted at, sworn at, ridiculed and lectured to, but never, as far as I can remember, were we bullied.

I see television programmes now, and I can honestly say that my experiences of basic training bore no resemblance to how they present it. The whole life was tough, but I always found it fun. I really did start to feel like a man, instead of that pathetic creature that I had been throughout school. I loved the life from the very start, and the 'runs ashore' with a bunch of mates were to be looked forward to throughout the rigours of the day.

We had to wear the awful, basic uniforms that we were issued with, and glass-shined boots to go ashore, (even from shore establishments like this it was always known as 'on board' or 'ashore'), and dancing, at the Portsmouth dance halls, in boots, must have caused agonies to the local females.

It was essential, in Service life, that we should all be as alike as possible; uniformed automatons, with as little individual identity as was feasable; all marching to the same music and in the same direction, tallist on the right, shortest on the left. As we got to know each other, we discovered that we were all there for a very wide variety of reasons, and from a myriad of different backgrounds. One thing, however, was remarkably noticeable. In the whole of my Service career I never met a single person who was there out of a sense of patriotism, or desire to serve 'Queen and Country.'

Getting the first haircut, at the barracks barbers, was hilarious, and it was after that experience that I got my name 'Glenn'. I had befriended a guy from Edinburgh, by the name of Tom Turnbull. He was older than all the rest of our class, because he had done his National Service in the army, and had then decided that he wanted to be a regular in the Navy. We were all signed up for seven years, though we were joined by a couple of National Servicemen at some point.

Although I knew that I would lose my 'Brylcreemed' DA, it was still a traumatic moment. It felt like real pain as my old identity fell about my shoulders and cascaded onto the floor. I think I knew what Charles the First must have felt like. When we emerged from the 'shearing shed' with our new, corporate identities, Tom said that I looked like Glenn Miller, (the only resemblance really was my rimless glasses), and he was going to call me Glenn from then on. It caught on with everyone else, and so I have been Glenn ever since.

Kitting out was equally hilarious, and after I left the barracks it was quickly into a naval tailors to get some wearable clothing. At that time the medical branch wore an Officer style, buttoned jacket, ordinary trousers, a white shirt and collar and a peaked cap, – white in the summer and black in the winter. We were issued with two uniforms, single-breasted, rough serge, and they looked awful. That issued gear spent the rest of my time in the Navy in my kit-bag.

We were also issued with a hammock, which we had to cart around with us everywhere we went. I never, ever slept in it, and I was never so pleased as I was on the day when ships got fitted out with bunks, and the hammock was handed back in, a few years later.

After six weeks we were transported to the railway station, an excited gaggle, each with kit-bag, hammock and small attache case, on our way to the Royal Naval Hospital, Stonehouse, Plymouth, to do our nursing training.

The hospital was a very old, stone built establishment. Like Dartmoor prison, it had been built by French prisoners during the Napoleonic Wars. In spite of its age and provenance, it was a comfortable, and very pleasant place to live and work, and I soon settled in. I enjoyed the great camaraderie of mess living, with the close proximity of friendly mates. There was a lot to do in the hospital, and I played rugby, football and tennis. Since I was still English at that point, I even played cricket.

It was such a friendly place, and I felt, for the first time in my life, that I was fitting in. My health was excellent, with no sense of being ill at all, and I soon forgot that I had ever had anything wrong with me. I was able to converse with people on my own terms, and express my opinions without being made to look stupid. Naval discipline was rigid, but generally, with good purpose, and strangely, in spite of it I had a great sense of freedom. I could go ashore with a bunch of the boys, or with the pal that I had made, and I was free to go where I liked and be my own mentor.

During the nursing course I was doing well. For once I was aware of learning, and enjoying what I was learning. My poor education did not seem to be standing in my way, and I could feel my confidence building daily.

Before I went into the Navy, I did not have a regular girlfriend. I had been a part of a group of friends, boys and girls, who just hung around together. We played tennis; went to a lot of dances; to the pictures together, and only one pair of the gang was a regular couple. I had been out with one of the girls a couple of times, a girl called Rosie, but it was not a relationship. In Plymouth, I also tended to go around in a group, and, although I had been to some dances with mates, and picked up girls for the evening, I was, likewise, uncommitted. So when I went home on my first leave, at Easter, there was no-one I was going home to. I hadn't been away long, but once the novelty of seeing me in uniform had worn off, I found myself an outsider. There were more pairings, and the activities did not include me. I did take Rosie out, once, and then that, very casual, relationship died too. It was a boring leave, and I was pleased when it ended and I was back in Plymouth. I think most of the other guys had had similar experiences.

Well into our training, and involved in hospital ward experience at that stage, we were beginning to feel like real nurses. Our uniform sleeves were still badgeless, and we were all working hard on exam preparation, which would, if passed of course, see a Geneva Cross, on a white circle inside a gold-wire ring on our right sleeves. Our preliminary nursing training complete, we would be away for our summer leave. Exams will have been passed and there would be very little to do at the hospital when we returned, apart from some further ward-time to gain some practical experience before being drafted to our respective Port Division hospitals – Haslar, at Gosport, for the Portsmouth division; RNH (Royal Naval Hospital), Gillingham, for the Chatham ratings, and some would remain in Plymouth.

I would be going to Chatham. In late July, summer leave started, and we were taken to Plymouth station in hospital transport. I boarded the train for St Pancras. In London I would then get a train on to Leicester, and then a four mile bus journey home.

Arriving at St Pancras station, I felt very tall, smart, and was flushed with pride in my new uniform. There was time to kill before my train to Leicester, so I made my way across the station to a small station cafe.

Railway stations, in the days of steam, were dirty, noisy, smelly places. Whistles were blowing, people were shouting, steam was hissing. There were always clanking sounds, and the noise of porter's barrows, with iron-rimmed wheels being pushed along, and the wonderful, masculine, VRUM, VRUM, VRUM, of engines leaving platforms. All held in under the high dome of the station roof.

People jostled each other, as they hurried to their various destinations, and people always seemed to look more exciting than they do on stations now, because travel was exciting.

Stations were soot-smeared, wherever you went. I can remember starting out on journeys looking immaculate, and arriving home with a black-spotted shirt, with a collar like a well-used dish-rag.

The cafe was small, cramped, and not very clean. There were large aluminium teapots on the counter, and a hissing machine that dispensed hot water. Railway sandwiches were notorious, and you only bought them if you were absolutely starving.

I asked for a black coffee. A splodge of tarry 'Camp coffee' was poured, into a stained cup, from a catering size bottle with a label bearing the picture of a kilted Scottish soldier, being waited on by a turbaned black servant, outside a tent, which was probably supposed to be in India. The picture, and the rest of the bottle were being slowly obscured by the volcano runs of brown, sticky, chicory essence, masquerading as coffee. Some hissing hot water was added to it, and I found somewhere to sit.

I arrived at the platform, just too late to hear a station announcement that mentioned Leicester. I approached a porter to ask if the train standing at the platform was the one for Leicester. He was not a happy-looking soul, as he stood staring at nothing, in his double-breasted, soot-black uniform, with a L.N.E.R. Badge on his peaked cap.

'Excuse me, is this the Leicester train?'

'Fackinell, s'jast bin annaanced; you fackin deaf?'

I wanted to thump him, but I restrained myself, and asked again.

'Frant free carridges,' he spat, and turned from me in disgust, with, 'fack me.'

Clearly his return to 'civvie street,' after he had freed the world from tyrany, had not come up to expectations.

I looked for a carriage that was free of a 'NO SMOKING' sign on the window.

I climbed the two steps into the carriage, and scrunched my way along the linoleum covered, gritty, floor of the side corridor, looking for an empty compartment. The train wasn't busy, and there were plenty of seats, and I found a compartment with only two people in it; a young girl, sitting by the window, and someone else. I slid open the compartment door, and entered. As I slid the door closed, it was like instant deafness; all the noise was shut out.

Railway compartments were wholly coloured tobacco-brown, whatever colour they had started life with. They had a special railway carriage smell – beneath the overwhelming nicotine smell, was a mixture of sweat, urine and coal-smoke. The seats were of some hard-wearing woven fabric, that had once been a pattern of different colours, but was now just a dirty brown, covered in various stains, that did not invite too much close thought. This one was at least tidy, so I suspected that this was its first use of the day.

I swung my small hand-case up onto the string-net luggage rack, next to a large suitcase, that I presumed belonged to the young girl, as the other person was sitting at the sliding-door end of the bench seat. I placed my cap, badge facing outward, on the rack next to my case. I cannot now, for the life of me, remember whether the other person was a man or a woman. I sat in a seat opposite the young girl. I do remember smiling at her, and I was aware that she was looking at my brand-new, shiny doeskin uniform, with the red cross on the sleeve. I was pleased, because I was so proud of the uniform, and I felt at the top of the world, and brimming with confidence.

After I was seated, I slid a packet of 'blue-liners' from the left pocket of my jacket. (Special, RN issued non-branded cigarettes, with a broad navy-blue band around the white packet, with R.N. In large print above it). I slid the inner part from the packet, lifted a cigarette into an offering position, and held the packet out to the girl.

'No thank you,' she almost whispered, smiling bashfully.

I put the cigarette between my lips; reached into my right pocket; produced a box of Swan Vestas, and lit my cigarette, blowing a cloud of smoke into the air. I blew out the match, and dropped it onto the floor, to start the day's detritus, that would no doubt build up with time. The cast metal ashtrays were stuffed solid with brown-stained cigarette ends, matchsticks and silver-paper, and looked as if they had been that way for years.

I stood up, and taking the two clasps in the centre of the sliding window in my fingers, I slid them open to the marked arrow that indicated 'ventilation.' The noises of the station assailed us instantly, but at least my smoke would be carried out of the window once the train got under way. In the meantime, I flapped my hand about to disperse it.

We were soon talking, and I told her about my encounter with the porter, and we laughed. It was the badge on my sleeve that opened the conversation, proper, because she wanted to know what it represented. When I told her that it meant that I was a nurse in the Navy, she told me that she was also training to be a nurse. What we talked about after that, neither of us has the slightest idea, but we must have talked all the way to Leicester, where she was also getting off. I told her that my name was Tony, because that's who I still was, away from the Navy, and she introduced herself as Pauline.

Pauline was sixteen years old then, and I was eighteen. She said she liked my uniform, and told me that it suited me. More flattering she could not have been, considering how I felt about it. (Amazingly, Pauline never saw me wearing any other clothing than that uniform, until June 2012, because, back in 1954, Royal Naval personnel were not allowed to wear civilian clothes).

What happened to the other occupant of that compartment, I have absolutely no idea. Pauline said that it was a woman, and that she left the train somewhere before Leicester.

The both of us remembered well, the important details of what happened after we left the train, because I took her to the pictures. The cinema was one of those small, one-feature places called a 'Cameo', and I think it was a part of the station complex. (I know there are Cameo cinemas now, but I don't think they are the same as the one that we went to, in 1954. I can't really say, because I've never been in one). They were small cinemas that had not long been opened, and were intended for passengers to relax in, during long waits for connections, and they were very inexpensive.

I don't know what it is with me and some movies that I have seen, but I remember that the film we saw was 'The Charge of The Light Brigade', with Errol Flynn. What neither of us could remember was what we did with our luggage. I only had a small hand-case, but Pauline was leaving Bath, and going home for good, so she had quite a large case, with all her belongings in it.

Other things we were able to recall , vividly. We really did sit on the back row, and there were no preliminaries before we were in each others arms. It was also not long before I started to explore the contours of her body, but remember, this was 1954, and the 'swinging sixties' were still to be invented, so my exploration was confined to the northern regions, only. Convent educated, Pauline, thought that this wasn't really the thing to be doing, but she said, later, that she wasn't too sure what to do about it, and, anyway, she was enjoying it, and didn't really want it to stop. For my part, I was aware that I had never done anything like this in my life before.

I had certainly changed into someone very different to that pathetic creature that had left home such a short time before.

On leaving the cinema we made our way to St Margarets bus station. The bus service for Melton

Mowbray was less frequent than the one to Scraptoft, so we had to hurry to be in time for Pauline to make it for the last bus. In spite of the fact that we arrived in plenty of time, Pauline almost missed the bus, because, reluctant to part, we were blissfully wrapped in each other's arms and didn't notice the bus about to pull away, and she had to leap for it. (We still could not recall what was happening to our luggage. We could only presume that it had been loaded on to the bus, before we enacted our farewell). The conducter grabbed her arm and helped her onto the bus, laughing, and saying 'eh up me duck,' because that's the way people greet each other in Leicester. No matter what the situation; whether you are male or female, you will always be 'me duck.'

She had told me where she lived, and how to get there, before we parted, and I promised to see her the following day.

She had another bus to catch, from Melton Mowbray to Scalford, before she arrived home. And she told me that her sister, Dorothy, going home from a date, was on that bus too.

'Where on earth have you been?' she asked Pauline, 'You were supposed to have been home ages ago. Dad was going mad when I left home this-afternoon, and mum was threatening to murder you. They're not very happy about you leaving Bath, so you are seriously in for it.'

Pauline did not enlighten her as to where she had been, and she said that she didn't care what was to happen, because she was so happy; to be going home, and because she had met me. When she got home, however, she escaped the threatened murder, because her mother was in bed, and her father was just on his way up, but he gave her something to look forward to in the morning, with dire warnings of her impending doom. She may have escaped dismemberment that night, but there were many sufferings she had to endure over the next few months.

I caught my bus home, in a trance I think. I had never felt as I did then, over anyone or anything. Pauline was such a gentle, beautiful young creature, and I really did know that she was something very special. It was the beginning of an enthralling relationship, which, sadly was to last for only a year.

CHAPTER 5

When I had left Pauline, as she had boarded her 'Lincoln Green' to Melton Mowbray, and we had blown kisses to each other through the barrier of glass that was between us, in July 1954, I think we both knew that we were on the verge of something special.

We were, I know, looking back on what happened, just a pair of easily excited teenagers. It is probable that every person on earth has had the same feelings. But, that was not how it felt to us then, or how it felt to us when we came together again, fifty eight years later. Both of us kept those memories alive, as something different to any other memories we had.

I boarded my 'Midland Red' for the four mile journey home. My mood was instantly elevated even higher when the conductor asked, 'Where to, Jack?' 'Jack!' That sounded good. Could life get any better?

When I arrived home, it was quite late, and my mother asked me why I was so late. I presume I must have told her; there was no reason not to, as far as I can remember. I still had my old bedroom, upstairs next to the bathroom, and looking out over the, quite large, back garden that we had. It was a modern house that we lived in, 1930's built, and it was a very pleasant, three bedroom house; it was a marvel that my mother had been able to afford to buy it, after renting it for about twenty years. My sister, two years younger than me, was still living at home with my mother, and had the single bedroom. There was very little change at home, but I had only been away for six months, so it was unlikely to have changed. However, there was one big change that I didn't notice at first; my mother had bought a television. TV was still very new, and probably less than half the population had one. It was a very small screen, about nine inches, and had only two channels, which were in black and white. Sometimes Pauline and I sat by my mother watching TV. Pauline sat on my lap, in an armchair, and we both remembered doing things, as we sat there, that we definitely should not have been doing, sitting next to my mother.

Neither of us could recall very much of what we did when I was at home, other than what went on in the bedroom. I had a 'Dansette', portable record player up in my room, and we spent some time up there listening to my music. Pauline said that I had a lot of Glenn Miller records, but I'm afraid her memory was playing tricks on her. I only had one Glenn Miller – 'Moonlight Serenade,' his signature tune. I think that Pauline was led into thinking that I liked Glenn Miller because of my adopted name. Music was not the big deal among teenagers that it is now, and my music was mostly jazz. Pauline says that she doesn't like jazz.

Before I had gone into the Navy, I had been very fond of dancing, and was out around twice a week, with friends, at regular dance halls. Since the television hadn't taken hold, at that time, dancing was still very popular, with live bands, and they were cheap to enter. But I don't think that Pauline and I ever went dancing at all. We did go to the cinema, several times, and occasionally we went on 'mystery bus tours.' A mystery because you did not know where the tour was going. You just paid your money and went; where to was never of much interest to us, anyway, because it was never anything more than an excuse to sit at the back of the bus, locked in each other's arms. Places for intimate contact were limited when my mother was at home.

I did have some girlfriends before I went into the Navy, but never anything serious, or steady. Morality was, supposedly, strong, and free-love was a long way off. However, morality and puritanism, came as a package deal along with hypocrisy, and though every male saw it as some kind of conquest to 'deflower' maidens, he also wanted to marry a virgin, and any girl who had lost her 'honour' would be very concerned if her relationship broke down, because it was not an envious position to be in as 'soiled goods.' That is why there was an, unwritten, legal contract, in fact, between engaged couples, and any man who broke an engagement could be sued for 'Breach of Promise.' (Come to think of it, it was probably written, and a fact in Law. Maybe, even still is).

I suppose I am still stuck in that time, in so many ways. I think I would find it difficult to make love to a body that was a copy of the Cistine Chapel ceiling, and which had been flashed to most of the tourists patrolling the bars of Benidorm.

The greatest consideration af all was that we had very little money, but it was amazing how far we managed to make it stretch. My first apprenticeship pay was fifteen shillings per week, (Seventy five pence). In the Navy we were paid fortnightly, and it was not very much, and for most of the time I went with Pauline we did very little that cost money. The cinema sometimes, or a coffee in the bus-station cafe, was about it.

That second day of my leave, when I went to Scalford was a walk in the fields and some time in Melton Mowbray.

I arrived at the farm in the afternoon. Pauline was surprised to see me.

'I didn't think you'd really come,' she said.

'Why, I told you I would be here? Didn't you want to see me?'

'Yes, I did, but I just didn't think you were serious. You didn't seem to be very serious yesterday.'

Even though she may not have been expecting me, it was Pauline who had answered the door when I knocked, and she came outside, and as we were standing talking I remember Richard appearing from somewhere, with his arm in a sling. We talked for awhile with Richard and then we went into the farmhouse.

The kitchen was a typical, large, farmhouse kitchen. There may have been an Aga range, but I can't really remember, but there was a large range of some kind, and a large, scrubbed top, wooden table, with wooden chairs. There were no formal introductions to her parents; little more than nods from them, actually, and I felt the tension. I think I did speak to them at some time; I can't remember anything about it, though, but I certainly was aware of the barrier between us. Pauline's mother was particularly frosty.

'Where are you planning going, young lady?' asked her mother.

'We're just going to take 'Sheila' out for a walk, first,' replied Pauline. Sheila was a copper coloured retriever. 'Then we'll probably go into Melton.'

I left my cap in the kitchen, and we set off across the farmyard, and through a farm gate into a small field containing cattle. The cows were grouped, as cows always seem to be, around a tree in a left corner of the field, swishing their tails and pushing and shoving each other, and making repulsive 'slomphing' noises, with feet and mouths, as they turned to watch us walk gingerly across the field, avoiding the obvious signs of their presence all around us. Sheila was running about all over the place, excitedly sniffing at things, and obviously joyful at being out. Before we reached another gate at the far side of the field, Sheila had already anticipated us, and gone through a hole in the hedge into the next field.

It was an expansive meadow sloping down away from us, and the grass was fairly long, and littered with meadow flowers, mainly of yellow and blue, but with spots of red like an impressionist painting. It was a beautiful day, with only the tiniest breeze moving the grass. Pauline and I held hands and swung across the field with that freedom that you always get in moments like that; days made to be young in. My double-breasted uniform jacket swung open, unbuttoned. We stopped at times when our eyes would meet, we'd laugh and we would pull into each other and embrace. I couldn't remember ever being so complete. In such a short time our lives had come together to stay together. We both knew it and we both felt it. Though, during our moments of recall later, there was so little that we remembered of that year together. I think the black clouds of the end of that year hung so heavily over us, that so much was blanked from our minds.

That day in the meadow was one of the iconic ones, though, and something that we both remembered clearly. Pauline was wearing a voluminous light fawn skirt, which she swung about her as she walked/skipped across that field. She also had on a white blouse, which buttoned up the front, and the hint of her light-blue bra was just discernable. She had very few clothes, actually, because she couldn't afford to buy a lot, and had to rely on parents for what she had. She never wore trousers, always a skirt or a dress. Don't forget, jeans hadn't become a part of our lives then.

Sheila had quietened down, and stayed closer to us running about our feet and stopping occasionally to sniff something that was particularly interesting, and when Pauline and I, out of sight of the farmhouse decided to lie on the grass, Sheila lay by the side of us with her head on her paws, but not before she had lolloped around us, face-licking and scampering, and wagging her whole body with her tail, thinking that this was to be some kind of game.

When I looked back on it, so many times over those long years, I always hovered above us, looking down on two ecstatic teenagers, wholly oblivious to anything beyond that spot on the planet. The length of the grass meant that we would need to sit up a little to see anything beyond where we lay. The smell of the grass and the earth, with a slight fungus hint of mushrooms, pervaded, and the faint smell of perfume from Pauline's throat made me feel dizzy. Nothing else existed. It was as if someone had just lowered that meadow out of the sky for our exclusive use, and when we left it, it would be taken back up again.

I took off my jacket, folded it inside out so as not to spoil the doeskin, and placed it beneath Pauline's head. (She kept sliding off it, so we dispensed with it very quickly). Since the previous day, when we had first met, our relationship had changed already.

As we lay there together, a future had joined us. We were passionately rolling into each other, and we were both very aroused, but we knew that there would be no casual sex. I did caress her body, and I stroked her gently, but not a button or zip fastener was undone. We both wanted it to happen, and we both knew that it would happen, but not on that occasion. Pauline told me that she believed, from that moment on, that we would be married.

That time in the meadow seemed to go on for ever; we wanted it to. Exhausted, physically and emotionally, and holding trembling hands, we lay looking up at the sky. Birds were wheeling above us, and we could hear them singing, and the grass rustling gently in the breeze.

'Could I have one, please?' Pauline asked, as I took a 'blue-liner' from a packet.

'What? You want a cigarette?' I asked, surprised. ' Have you ever smoked before?'

'No, but it looks nice. I'd like to try it.'

She took the cigarette, and I lit it for her. I watched her closely as she inhaled the smoke. Her hand swung up to her face, and she tried to suppress a cough, waving her hand about in front of her face to try and disperse the exhaled smoke.

'Well?'

'It's OK', she spluttered, struggling to restore her breathing,' I'll get used to it.'

Pauline did get used to it, and, I'm ashamed to say, that day I started her smoking. (Ironically, I gave up smoking cigarettes a short time later. Pauline gave up, with an enormous struggle, in her sixties).

We rolled towards each other for a last embrace before rising. Sheila sensed the movement and began to stretch before getting to her feet, and a good shake. I pulled Pauline to her feet, and we brushed ourselves down with our hands to remove any stray grass from our clothes. Pauline turned around, and I brushed down the back of her, before she did the same for me. Opening up my still folded jacket, I gave it a shake and put it over my arm to carry. Pauline straightened my tie – yes, I had on my white uniform shirt and black tie – and, holding hands, we set off towards the farmhouse, two different people to the ones who had come that way an eternity before.

When we arrived back at the farmhouse, we found Pauline's dad wearing my cap, and parading around the kitchen in it, while Pauline's mum looked on with utter disdain, and disapproval. Looking very sheepishly at me, he snatched my hat from his head, and placed it back on the table, with a little embarrassed cough. I smiled at him, and he gave half a smile back. I think, that away from the dominance of his wife, he and I could have got on. Pauline thought that too, and she said, only recently, that she thought her dad came to realise the mistake they made in splitting us up.

I can tell you very little, in detail, of that year we had together, because, apart from the iconic moments that had special meaning, the rest all seemed to take place in my bedroom, and I am sure you will understand when I decline to enlighten you about that. Pauline remembered some things that I did not, and sometimes it was vice versa. She remembered a bus trip that we went on with two pre-Navy friends of mine, David and Sheila, to Stratford-Upon-Avon, with time spent on the river in small rowing-boats.

I remembered a time, when we had been together for nearly a year. We had gone into the fields by my house, and taken a walk to a rabbit warren, close by. The rabbits darted for their holes as we approached, which caused Pauline to laugh. That was an old haunt of mine, and I knew that if we were very still and quiet the rabbits would soon come out again.

We sat, quietly, in a depression in the ground just below the warren and watched through the tall grass. Very soon the little faces of the rabbits started to appear at the entrances to their holes, and after looking around they emerged into the sunlight. They played, and ran about and chewed grass, all within about ten feet of us. They often looked up, and I am sure that they knew we were there, but they seemed to have taken it upon themselves to trust us.

Since we had been together nearly a year, our relationship had moved on a long way from that similar moment in the meadow on our first outing together, and this was a mood not to be wasted. As we sat Pauline and I leaned into each other, and as we lay back on the ground we started to caress, and the rabbits watched us make love. That was a moment that we both remembered vividly.

I went back there quite recently. It was the first time I had been back in over sixty years. It is an area that hasn't changed in all that time, and although I didn't see any rabbits, the evidence of the warren was still there, with bare patches of earth where their holes used to be. I sat in the grass, and I wept, as I watched us making love there.

Both Pauline and I remembered the first time we made love. It wasn't on that first summer leave, it was a long-weekend just a short time after I had returned to Plymouth from that leave. We worked three watches in the hospital. I can remember the finishing times, but not the starting times of each watch, and we worked over two weekends in each month, and the other two were a short weekend, from 1300 Saturday to 0700 Monday, and a long weekend from 1300 Friday to 1300 Monday. I could never get home on short weekends, which meant that I would only see Pauline once a month, so we made the best of it.

That particular weekend was in August, 1954, and it was my last at Plymouth, as I was drafted to RNH Chatham, in late August. As servicemen had very poor pay, it was common practice to hitch-hike home when we went on weekend leave, because we were not entitled to a railway warrant. Plymouth was quite a long way from Leicester, and although we never had any problems getting lifts, because motorists and truck drivers were very understanding towards us, (men from all the services were a common sight on the roads back then), it was very late when I arrived home, and everyone was in bed, including Pauline, who had come during the day to stay the weekend. She had my bedroom, and my sister had moved in with my mother to surrender her bedroom to me.

I crept up the stairs and quietly went into my bedroom. It was a fairly light night and I could see Pauline's head on the pillow in the light from the window. She stirred and opened her eyes as I looked down on her. Blinking, her whole face smiled at me. She looked so beautiful and peaceful there, and I knelt beside the bed and kissed her. She made a lovely little noise.

'I was getting worried,' she whispered.

'Some slow lifts,' I replied, and her arms came from under the covers, and she put them around my neck and pulled me to her. She was wearing her old school pyjamas, and I laughed. She gave me a punch, and told me not to laugh at her. As we kissed, I slid my hand beneath the bedclothes and began to caress her body, and as she moved to me my hand moved into previously unexplored places. We were ready. Pauline knew and I knew.

'Please come into the bed,' she whispered, and I began to undress. I needed a bath, (we didn't have a shower), but there was no way that I was going to have one. Time could not be wasted. I slipped quietly into the bed, and we embraced tightly, before I removed her pyjama top. After a little while I took off her pyjama bottoms, and, after more gentle caressing, we made love.

The very first time for both of us. It was not awkward or fumbling or embarrassing. That moment was the most natural act between two people in love. I cannot imagine a first time being any more beautiful, gentle, passionate and loving. I relived that moment many times in the following years.

After that first time my memory recalls very little else other than our frequent love-making, whenever we were together. How she never became pregnant is miraculous, as the only protection we ever practised was 'interruptus.'

There was one moment from my bedroom that remains vividly in my mind, because it was such an epiphany. It was an afternoon, (when in the calendar I can't remember), and we had the house to ourselves. Pauline had got out of bed, and I lay there watching her. There was a long mirror on the wall beyond the foot of the bed, and Pauline stood before it examining and preening her naked body. She had her back half towards the mirror, and was looking over her shoulder, running her fingers slowly over her body from her waist and down over her hips, as she examined her back in the mirror.

I gasped in a breath and then stopped breathing altogether. It is impossible to describe how I felt, and the nearest I can get to it is to say that it was like the feeling I had when I saw the wondrous beauty of the 'Pieta' in The Vatican for the first time, but gazing on Pauline was much more intense and personal, and the Pieta did not have those little brown moles. Her body was sculpted to absolute perfection. Through the haze I tried to comprehend how blessed I was at that moment.

Through the winter of 1954 and into the spring of 1955, I went home on my monthly long weekends, and my Christmas leave. Pauline was at my house for Christmas day, and we enjoyed the dinner that my grandmother had prepared, next door.

I was never at 'Wolds Farm' again; Pauline said that her parents were wholly against our relationship, and she was scared that if I went back there they would be so unpleasant to me that she was afraid I would leave her. I had the feeling that there was more; I sensed that Pauline was actually afraid of her father. I asked her if he ever hit her, and she was evasive, and wanted to change the subject. I told her that I did not want to cause a major break between her and her family, and I said that if he ever hit her I would end it between us, because I couldn't be there to protect her, and I couldn't bear to think of her being hurt because of me. She cried, then, and said,

'Please Tony, everything's alright, I promise. Please don't leave me. I don't think I could stand it. I love you, Tony, and I think we should get married as soon as possible, then they won't be a problem any more.'

Early in the spring of 1955, I think it was actually still February, I was to be away from Pauline for around six weeks. A member of staff at the Royal Naval Hospital in Simonstown, South Africa, was on the way home on compassionate leave. I was sent for and told that I was to go out there as a temporary replacement. It wasn't known, at that point, how long I would be there, so when I informed Pauline, we had no idea how long I would be away. I had to go before I could even see Pauline, but she phoned me, and we had a very tearful fairwell.

I'll never forget my arrival at Simonstown, and getting off the plane into sweltering heat, in my UK winter uniform. The journey to the hospital was very unpleasant, even with my jacket and tie off, and I was never so pleased than I was when I was issued with tropical kit.

I could have done with a break to recover, but I was on a ward, and working, very soon after I arrived. Very little of what happened there has remained in my memory, except for the one thing that has driven everything else out of my mind. I do remember sitting down to write to Pauline, though, as soon as I'd had a shower, and settled into the mess.

I made a friend very quickly. He was someone I had known back in the UK actually, at Chatham hospital, so he was not a stranger. On one afternoon, a few days after I arrived, Larry and I had a 'make-and-mend', (afternoon off), and he offered to show me around Cape Town. I know that we went for a meal, and into a bar in the evening, but most of everything else escapes me, except that I was attracted to a jewellers shop, and I thought I might buy something to take back to Pauline.

What I bought was a diamond solitaire engagement ring!

Pauline sometimes wore a small signet ring on the third finger of her right hand, and one day, when we had been lying in a field back home, I had removed the ring from her right hand and replaced it on her left hand.

'There, we're engaged now. We are joined for life,' I had said. She was so delighted with it that she had kept it there the whole day, but later, when she put it back on her right hand before she went home, she tried to put it on my finger, first. Even though I had slender fingers then, they weren't that thin. She did, however manage to get it on my 'pinky.' It was a bit tight, but when I was in that jewellers in Simonstown, when I was asked the size of the ring I wanted, I knew by trying it on my little finger. The ring was white gold, and I had never seen white gold before, as it did not seem to be in circulation in the UK at that time. It must have been something quite new.

Not many letters had been exchanged between us while I was there, because the mail seemed to take ages to get to the UK. I couldn't wait to get home, and to get engaged to Pauline. I knew what it meant to me, and had a very good idea what it would mean to her, but the six weeks seemed to go on forever. But when I did get home I went straight on Easter leave.

Pauline was at the station in Leicester to meet me off the train, and we were both in tears as we clutched each other, afraid that the world had shut us out, I think. On the bus to my house, we were on the top deck, alone, and we instantly started to make love, as we always did when we got on that bus. (I have often thought back to those moments, and wondered if they had that mirror at the top of the stairs then, so that the conductor could see up to the top deck).

We were reckless, and invisible to the world. No-one but ourselves existed, and we were oblivious to anyone, and anything beyond where we were. There may even have been other passengers up on the top deck of the bus. We just didn't see them. I loved her, and that day we were going to be engaged to be married.

When we arrived home we went up to my bedroom to deposit Pauline's overnight bag. We fell onto the bed, clinging together like ivy to a tree, but my mother was downstairs, because it was a weekend and she wasn't at work, so we unjoined fairly quickly, before we were tempted to throw caution to the wind.

Before we went downstairs, I told Pauline to close her eyes. I held her hands for a moment; I kissed her, and I held the open box, containing the engagement ring, in my hand, and asked her to open her eyes. The blood seemed to drain from her face, and I thought she was going to pass out, so I reached out to her and I held her. She had the ring in her hand, and I felt the enormous sobs coming from her, and felt the tears on my neck. I whispered into the back of her ear,

'Will you marry me?' I released her from the embrace so that I could look into her face. She couldn't speak; she held out her left hand and gave me the ring to put onto her finger. There was another enormous sob and a huge wet smile as she held me again, and said,

'Oh, Tony, I love you so much. I love you so much, and it's a beautiful ring. Thank you, Oh thank you Tony.'

It was the afternoon, and it was a lovely sunny day, and we passed my mother, busy in the kitchen, and went outside and sat on the lawn. My sister, Elizabeth, came out and started asking about South Africa, and how we were, and all the usual kind of greetings. I think my mother had noticed that Pauline had been crying, and had sent Elizabeth out to find out what was wrong, but Pauline's face was able to reassure her that nothing was amiss.

I'll never forget that picture of Pauline sitting on the lawn, with her legs drawn up under her widespread skirt just gazing at her ring, the diamond glinting in the sunlight. My sister would have needed to be blind not to notice, and it was not long before she was running, screaming, into the house,

'Mum, mum, Tony and Pauline are engaged!'

My mother raced out, wiping her hands on her pinafore, demanding to see the ring. She was genuinely delighted, because she had become very fond of Pauline.

Here in Scotland, as many well know, we have an inbuilt, immovable pessism, and even though I wasn't born Scots, I succumbed to its infectiousness very quickly. When the weather is glorious, we are known to say, 'aye, it's fine noo, but we'll pay for it later!' or if, by some miracle, our national football team wins a game, the bar-room pundit will always declare, 'that's fine, but we'll be hammered in the next game.' Happiness sits heavily on our shoulders, and if I had been a Scot in 1955, seeing that wonderful happiness in Pauline, and feeling happier than

I had ever felt in my life, I know I would have said, 'I am frightened. We are too happy. I feel that something bad is going to happen.' In 2013 I had been Scottish for a long time, and I said to Pauline, 'I'm scared, pet, I love you so much, and we are so happy. I think something bad might happen.'

CHAPTER 6

'Cause and effect.' 'Action and reaction.' Whatever we call it, we believe that things happen because something made them happen. Spontaneity, we know happens, but we still want to believe that there was something that created the circumstances for spontaneity to happen. Historians will start with the event. They will then spend many hours examining everything that led up to the event. There must be a cause, and no historian would go to bed happy until it was found. Case closed. Well, not quite, because when all the evidence has been gathered, we then need 'the spark;' that moment when the touch paper was lit which caused the explosion. What was it that finally did it?

When Pauline and I first came together, the day after meeting on the train, in that meadow in July 1954, the walls had closed around us and shut out the rest of the world. We had become encapsulated within our love for each other, and there was nothing else out there but us. We were invisible; we were bullet-proof. We never stopped loving each other, I'm convinced of that, but as time went on the walls moved out again, and the rest of the world began to play its part in our lives once more.

For me, I was experiencing my new life in the Navy. I was enjoying great new experiences, and living a life that I had never known before. There had never been any other time in my life when all my stars seemed to be in the ascendancy. My belief in myself had become so positive, and I was capable of anything.

At Chatham hospital my first assignment was to an acute medical ward. The wards were large, one room wards, with around thirty beds, arranged with fifteen down each side of the ward. All of the patients in that ward were very ill, many with terminal illnesses. A large number of the patients were old – Naval pensioners, who were entitled to medical care in a Naval hospital because of their previous service. All had served in the war. Even the younger patients were very ill, too. Death was almost a daily occurrence on that ward, and it was a harsh 'baptism' into nursing. Prior to this I had never even seen a dead person, and now I was laying them out on a regular basis. The loss of young men was particularly painful to experience. I tell you this only to help you to understand what my life was when I was away from Pauline.

Away from the ward, I had a social life. It was usually going out with mates, probably to a pub, or down to the NAAFI, to a dance. I met other women, and had opportunities, but I was never unfaithful to Pauline. The stress of the work made it essential that there was a relief from it.

I only got to see Pauline one weekend a month, and our regular method of communication was the old 'snail-mail,' and I was not a good letter writer. Pauline was, and her letters outnumbered mine by at least two to one. My, seeming, lack of care upset her. She told me, and I know that she thought that I may be seeing other girls. She, tearfully, asked me once, 'Tony when you tease me about all the Wrens and nurses that you know, you are just teasing, aren't you?'

'Yes, my love,' I replied, 'of course I'm just teasing you. I'm sorry, I'll try to be good in future.' I knew that it was something that troubled her, and I know that I should have been much more sensitive.

The walls that had enclosed us had moved out a long way, and our lives had moved very much back into the world again.

It was during my summer leave of 1955 that one of the most memorable events of our lives together occurred. Pauline had met me off the bus in Melton Mowbray, and it was a glorious sunny day, so we went to the park. (Why is it that the sun shone so often in those days?)

We lay on the grass, and oblivious to the other people around us, we embraced, and started to do things that should not be done in public. I lay on my back, and Pauline sat astride me with her face above me and her hands placed, one either side of my head, and as she leaned down to me and kissed me, I took advantage of that same voluminous fawn skirt that I told you about before, and made love to her. That skirt hid much sin at that moment. However, it was not the ideal place for us to satisfy our feelings, so we got up and walked some distance away from the public gaze, to the sloping bank of the river.

We were surrounded by bushes, and across the narrow river the other bank was also covered with shrubs. We began to make love very earnestly, and we both knew that we were not going to interrupt.

Pauline had said that she believed that the only way her parents would consent to her marrying before she was twenty one, would be if she was pregnant. (Looking back, I think it was twisted logic. What they would have done, I've no idea, but agreeing to us marrying would not have been their solution). We did not say 'OK let's do it.' No arrangements were made, but we knew that it was going to happen there, on that river bank. Getting close to climax, Pauline suddenly shouted, 'stop, Tony stop!' I was startled, and she said, 'there's someone watching us!' We were both trembling, and our passion slowly drained as I asked, sullenly,

'Where?'

'Across the river. In the bushes on the other bank.'

As I turned to look I caught a quick glimpse of a figure darting out of the bushes, and running away. Pauline said,

'The rotten pig, we were almost there.' The abject disappointment in her voice cut deeply into me, and I pulled her to me and kissed her. Unfortunately, the passion had abated; the moment was lost.

After we had adjusted our clothes, I held Pauline in my arms. She was tearful, but said nothing as she fused her body to mine. I felt very despondent, and so did she. A peeping Tom, though he never knew it, may have changed history at that moment.

We sat silently for a while, and then we rose, brushed ourselves down, and, holding hands, we set off into town. In a cafe, over coffee, Pauline swore that every man's face we saw in that place was the one she had seen looking through the bushes.

Slowly, our mood changed, from sullen, and depressed, and we began to see the funny side of it. We started to make jokes about the peeping Tom, and imagined all sorts of persona for him, and we were laughing. People in the cafe looked at us, holding hands, laughing, and being 'a sailor, out with his girlfriend.' People smiled, at each other and at us. We laughed a lot about it, much later, too. And it was always mentioned, and laughed about in our recent phone-calls, since coming back together.

That was close to the last time that I made love to Pauline. Her walls had moved out too, and she had a job, which cut down, considerably, the amount of time we had together. She was working in an office at an agricultural research establishment, and the hours were long. She didn't come to stay at my house ever again. We weren't drifting apart; we were as close, when we were together, as we had ever been, but things were happening; unexplained things, and it was fifty seven years before I was to discover the truth.

The last weekend of that summer leave, Pauline was to come to my house on the Sunday; for our last day together before I went back to Chatham. She didn't arrive.

I felt so low, and I thought over all the odd things that had happened during that leave.

What we don't know, we are inclined to make up, and using all the evidence available to us we always manage to come to entirely the wrong conclusion. I thought I was losing her, and in desperation, I phoned the farm. Because of the reception I usually got from her mother, (It was always her that answered the phone), I was shaking.

'Yes?' Her mother said. That was how she always answered the phone.

'Could I speak to Mary please?' I requested. I had been given a severe ear-pounding once when I asked for Pauline, so it had to be Mary.

'Mary, it's him!' She shouted. I heard Pauline coming to the phone and taking hold of the dangling receiver.

'What happened?' I asked.

Her voice was shaking as she answered. I could tell that she had been crying. I always knew from the way Pauline spoke when she had been crying.

'I'm sorry, I couldn't come. I'm really sorry, Tony.'

'Why? There must be a reason?'

I should have guessed that her mother would be hovering, listening to every word, but I just didn't think.

'I just couldn't. I can't tell you why; I'll tell you next time I see you. Write to me when you get back. Please.'

I hung up without saying anything more. The walls had suddenly just closed in again, but this time I felt imprisoned. I didn't have to be back until the following day, Monday, at 1800, so I packed what little I had on Monday morning, and I went out for a walk.

I was in terrible despair, and bewildered. I needed to get out of the house to try and make some sense of it as I walked. I didn't get very far up the lane towards the village of Scraptoft, when a bus passed ahead of me on the way down to the village. It had stopped at the end of the lane, and passengers alighted. Among them was Pauline. She was as surprised to see me as I was to see her. As she walked towards me she seemed unsteady on her feet, and I could see that she was in no state to be interrogated, so I took her hand and we walked back, in silence, to the house. Pauline was very upset, and I could see that she was worried. We were close, and I embraced her. The events of the previous day were not spoken of at all. When it was time to leave for the train, Pauline said that she wanted to go with me, and we got the bus together. No love-making this time!

It is no accident that so many cinematic moments have featured fairwells on station platforms, with the smoke and steam of the old steam-trains rising around the embracing couple, with a background noise, of hissing, and nasal station announcers over the tannoy, beneath a sooty high dome of glass that kept in the sounds, smells and steam. It seems such an improbable canvas for a romantic picture, but it was for farewells, and it could not fail to be romantic. That particular farewell remained, vividly, in my memory all my life, and Pauline said that it remained with her too.

I held Pauline so close to me, and the tears had a poignancy to them that they had never had before. The guard's whistle blew, and he leant out from the guard's-van to wave his green flag, and as that sudden upward rush of smoke from the engine's funnel shot skywards, I jumped for the open door of the train. Pauline was moving along the platform with the slow-moving train as I wrestled with the leather strap to lower the window. I leaned out and I took her in my arms and almost lifted her into the air, before letting her go as the train gathered speed with a 'whum, whum, whum…whum, whum, whum.' I leaned out as far as I could from the window, and we waved to each other until some time after we had lost sight. I flumped into my seat, and I knew that what I felt was not what I wanted to feel. There was a leaden ominousness in my heart.

There is a saying that 'things come in threes.' I think that saying must have been born out of the experience that sometimes it seems as if things come together, and they cause something bad to happen. These comings together, of unrelated things, is what history is really all about. I don't think major moments in history happened because of just one thing; it is like a chemical mix. The elements come together, by experiment or accident, and suddenly, it happens. It is all beyond our control, yet, nevertheless, it happens because of us. Our actions inter-relate with the actions of others. There are mistakes; misunderstandings and misinterpretations, and then, because of something indefinable, something happens.

Sometimes, as with my coming together with Rosemary, later on in my life, the outcome is, at least, acceptable. A collection of events was beginning to happen between Pauline and me. We could feel it happening without actually knowing that it was happening. If we had been able to see into the future, could we have prevented it? Every Shakespearean tragedy is about the failure, of some poor 'Hero,' to take control of his own destiny, and destiny seemed to have taken hold of us. What chance did we have?

When I got back to the hospital, I was pretty quick in writing a letter to Pauline, to tell her how much I loved her, and I made love to her in the letter, as I always did. I also got one from her, which she must have written at about the same time, saying much the same as I had said, and making love to me, too. I wasn't in much of a mixing mood, and spent a lot of time on my own; well, as much as is possible in a mess full of other men.

My temporary stay in South Africa had had side-effects, that didn't affect me much at the time, but were now beginning to take an ugly shape in my mind. The reason for the draft was because the person I was replacing had received a letter that some member of his family had written to him to tell him that his wife was pregnant. Since he had been in Simonstown for nearly a year, he applied for, and got, compassionate leave to go home and sort it out.

It was always a very big worry among the men in the Navy, that their wives/ girlfriends, may not be as loving as they seemed. It was made a joke of, and ribbing was rife, and 'Dear Johns' were posted on the mess noticeboard, for laughs, and added comments from other blokes in the mess, suggested what should be done to the offending females. It would be three weeks before I would get a long weekend, and I was starting to feel very lonely.

Without any warning, I was transferred from the

acute medical ward, to a zymotic, isolation section for pulmonary tuberculosis patients. I should have been flattered, because that was a plumb move, for the privileged few, with extra pay because of the infection risk, but it meant new procedures, new staff colleagues and new patients, and, the state of my mind at that point, made my life seem difficult, for no reason.

The failure of Pauline to turn up at my house, that Sunday, and the lack of explanation, still nagged at my mind. She had not explained it, as she had said she was going to do, and I hadn't raised it because she had been so upset.

Looking back, there was no doubt that that confluence of events was beginning to build.

It was in my second week back from leave that I got the letter from Pauline's mother. I didn't recognise the handwriting, but I certainly recognised the Melton Mowbray postmark. I kept the letter for a long time. I don't have it now so I can't quote it accurately, but I can remember very well what it said.

'Dear Mr Spiers,

My husband and I are becoming increasingly concerned at the way in which you are treating our daughter, Mary, who you know as Pauline. She spends so much time in tears, waiting for letters from you that never arrive. We feel that someone who has so little regard for her feelings is not a suitable match for our daughter, and we would like it to end now. I am aware that your relationship has gone much further than it should have done, and that there is talk of an engagement. This is quite ridiculous, at her age, especially as she is seeing a very nice boy in Melton when you are not here. He has much more consideration for her and treats her as a boy should treat a girl, and she is very happy with him. I would like you to stop seeing Mary now, and I do not think you should come to Melton, or try to contact her again.

    Grace Phizacklea.

I sat and stared at the letter, rather than reading it twice. At that first reading it was the first part of the letter that hit me the hardest, because it was true. I had been treating Pauline very badly, and I knew it. This was a reasonable letter from a concerned mother; one that I could imagine framing myself if it had been my seventeen year old daughter.

It was a 'cause and effect' letter; it said that what I had done had driven Pauline away from me. The first part, being true, must mean that the second part was also true. Even in the turmoil that my mind was going through, the misgivings that had begun to form in my mind were coming together. Standing largest in my head was the Sunday she had failed to turn up at my house. This explained it.

The distance between us that was evident during my last leave. This explains it. The wife of the man from Simonstown; the 'Dear Johns' on the notice board; my current insecurity. All of these things were starting to revive my old prejudices against women. 'Prejudice' – the 'knowledge' of the pig-ignorant. What I didn't know or understand, I started to make up. I saw her in bed with someone else, doing the things that we had done. It's amazing how the mind has to fly to extremes at times like that.

The poison started to circulate through me, and as it did my own part in what had happened was being removed from the equation, and it was becoming all her fault. Jealousy is, I think, the only emotion that is stronger than love. Murders have been committed in the name of love, but I think that most of them came from jealousy, not from love at all.

Was that letter the spark that lit the tinder? The catalist; whatever you want to call it. Pauline always maintained that it was, and she said that as soon as she heard about it, years later, she understood it, and she forgave me.

She spent so many years looking after her mother, and hating her for what she had done. Yes, she said, 'hating.' Her mother had invaded Pauline's privacy. She had gone into Pauline's bedroom, and taken the collection of letters that she had received from me, from the box that they were kept in, and she had read them. Pauline and I made love in our letters, so that was how her mother discovered that our relationship 'had gone further than it should have done.'

Pauline could not tell me at the time that her mother had done that, because it wasn't until long after I had dumped her that she found out about her mother's letter.

Me? I'm not so sure that it was the letter that did it. It

is possible to relive it, now, but it is not possible to get back into my head, and see what was going on in there. Whatever else, I should have given Pauline the chance of a defence, but I didn't. I accused her, tried her, found her guilty and punished her, without asking for an explanation. If I had asked her about what her mother had said, and discovered that her mother was lying, would it have changed anything? Pauline and I have talked it through, many times, and we both know that, not only would it have changed nothing, it would have ended everything between us for ever, and we would never have got back together, as we have done, now.

It was all about trust. Her mother could not have known it at the time, but her choice of method to separate us, could not have been better.

I hadn't told Pauline about the letter because of stupid male pride. I didn't want her to know that I had learned that she was seeing someone else. I wanted her to know that it was me dumping her and not her betraying me. Whatever the outcome, the letter had done its job; trust had been destroyed, and I don't think I would have believed Pauline's pleas of innocence.

It was more than a betrayal of trust, it was a huge blow to my confidence. After I had left home, I had risen to the top of the world. But my confidence was as fragile as a balloon. The balloon was punctured, and I plummeted to earth, the empty, useless thing I had been previously.

In the final analysis, it all happened, and it cannot be changed, so there is absolutely no point in mulling over it now. It was the end.

Less than two weeks after I received the letter I went

home. Pauline met me in Leicester. I had hitch-hiked, and as I picked up a regular lift from a truck driver, I was able to ring Pauline, when we stopped for a coffee, and tell her my approximate time of arriving in Leicester, and where I would be dropped off.

Pauline felt the tension, immediately, I could see it in her face, and I could also see that she was frightened. We did not make love on the bus to my house, but we held hands, and Pauline rested her head on my shoulders. On the Sunday we did make love, in my bed, even though my mother was downstairs. It was tender; even loving, and I knew that I was very close to speaking to Pauline about the letter.

Late Sunday afternoon Pauline went home, and said that she would be in Leicester to see me off the following day. I didn't ask how she was able to get off work. I phoned her to say what time I would be in Leicester, and she and I met near a truck depot, where I knew I would get my first lift.

We stood by a wall outside the depot. Pauline was wearing her ring. She was so quiet and submissive, and I had to work at being detached. I told her that as we weren't officially engaged, I wanted the ring back, and we would get properly engaged the next time I was home. She had told me that she had forgotten to take it off when she went home, the day I had given it to her, and she told me that her mother had seen it, and got very angry about it. That gave me the perfect excuse to take it back from her; to save her from further trouble at home. She had to tug at the ring to get it off. There were tears in her eyes as she handed it to me, and she looked up into my face. She was trying to hold back the tears, because she didn't want me to see them.

The truck I was hitching started to move out of the gateway, and the driver gave me a wave. I kissed Pauline, coldly, and I climbed up into the cab. As we pulled away I could see that she was sobbing deeply. I gave a half-hearted wave, and that was it; for fifty-seven years.

After I got back, I'm afraid I kept Pauline waiting about a week before I sent the letter dumping her. I was so cruel. And even now, talking about it makes me relive just how dreadful I was. What I said in the letter, I have shut out of my mind. Pauline told me that I did not say that I had stopped loving her. She said that I told her that I no longer saw a future for us together.

The reply I got from Pauline was heartrending, and I do remember so much of what she said. She was devastated, and the pain she was going through was so obvious in her letter. She just could not understand why I had done what I did. She asked if she could have her ring……I'm sorry, I can't go on with this. Recalling it now, just to tell you about it, is too painful for me.

It is hard to believe, now, that I was that person. (Pauline always cried whenever we spoke of it). I didn't reply to her letter, and when one of the guys in the mess was getting engaged, a short while later, just before I left the hospital, I sold him the ring for a fraction of what I had paid for it. I just wanted it out of my life.

Not long after Pauline's letter, I got the one from my mother, telling me that she never wanted to see me again. She said that Pauline was heartbroken.

'The grief in that poor child's face will go with me to the grave,' my mother said, 'You are an animal. I am ashamed to call you my son. May God forgive you for what you've done. I can't.'

I kept the three letters for years; the one from Pauline's mother, the one from my mother, and Pauline's last one. In fact I kept all of Pauline's letters. I don't have them anymore, I'm afraid. The small case that I kept them in was stolen from me, at one of the London railway stations, when I was passing through, some years later.

Back in Chatham, I spent very little time feeling sad, or guilty. The outside world beckoned, and I went. Most of my off-duty time was spent in bars, or dancing at the NAAFI. I had no particular friends, I just joined any hedonistic group that was passing. My deteriorating lifestyle was so obvious, because it was so out of character, and it soon caught the attention of the M.O. (Medical Officer), in charge of my section, Surgeon Commander Black. It was actually the ward sister who had alerted him to my deterioration. She had already given me the 'third degree,' and noticed that her lecture had had no noticeable effect. I was summoned to the inner chamber. I knocked at the door.

'Come in, Spiers.' He had seen that it was me through the partially open door. Commander Black was one of those officers who looked as if he had been made to fit his uniform, instead of the other way round. He always looked perfect, with the three gold rings on his sleeves; the deep red bands between them. He was as efficient as he looked, in everything he did, and as strict a disciplinarian as he was, he was greatly respected for his absolute professionism. He was even liked by most people, including me.

I stood to attention before his desk. He carried on looking over something, and then, putting whatever it was down on the desk, he looked at me. He stood up from his desk.

'At ease, Spiers.' ... 'You haven't been on this section for long, have you?'

'No sir.'

'Would it surprise you to know that you were recommended to me?' I looked at him with a look that indicated that I was, indeed, surprised.

'Well you were, and sister seems quite pleased with the way you have settled in, and I must say that, from what I've seen, you are doing a good job.'

'Thank you sir.' I had a good idea what was coming at that point. Praise rarely came without a 'but.'

'I suppose you are wondering why I've sent for you?'

'Yes sir,' I lied.

'Well, the thing is Spiers, sister is also very concerned about you. Not about the way you work. If that was the case I'd have you out of here in a jiffy. Sister feels that your lifestyle, off-duty, is a mess, and she is concerned that if it goes on, it will start to affect your work. Others have noticed it too, and I've made a few enquiries. As far as I can gather, you seem to be drunk more often than you are sober?' That was a real question, not a rhetorical one.

'Yes sir,' I muttered.

'Right, Spiers, well the thing is I am not having you on this section unless you buck your ideas up, understand?

I hope I wasn't mistaken in taking you on. I don't think I was, but it's now up to you to put it right.'

'Yes sir.'

'I have enrolled you on a promotion course, for your 'Leading Rate.' Maybe that will give you something better to occupy your time, and knock some of the stupid nonsense out of you. You are intelligent enough and efficient enough, and if you weren't, I wouldn't give a damn about you. This is not an offer, it's an order. Chief will give you the details. Do you understand?'

'Yes sir.' I was flabbergasted. I had guessed that I was going to get a bollocking, but I didn't expect that.

'Off you go.'

He was certainly sharp, and to the point, and he set off a new train of thought in my head. I had no intention of going away with a brand new aim in life. I was still carrying baggage, and even though I may not have been aware of it at the time, my separation from Pauline had cast me into a limbo that 'in one bound' I would be free of. Nevertheless, it was an experience that I had not had before. People, who I had always thought marginal in my life, noticed what I was doing, and cared. They did not need to. I was nothing to them, really.

It was a very pleasant feeling, actually, and I appreciated it, and it was the boost I needed to restore my confidence in myself.

Although it took a little time, I did make an effort to respond to it, and during the course that he had dragooned me on to, I did focus my attention on making sure that I passed. I knew that it was in my interests, and I also knew that if people take time and effort in your interests, then you would be stupid to pass up the opportunities offered. I don't think they would do it twice, if you didn't respond the first time. Well, Surgeon Commander Black wouldn't. He didn't suffer fools gladly.

The course did me a world of good, and occupied my mind. The restlessness in my head settled a lot, and I could stop feeling sorry for myself, and do something useful. I passed the exams with reasonable success, (I still have the certificate of my results, and they weren't bad, but should have been better), but even though I was qualified for the 'Leading Rate,' promotion was very slow, and it would be at least two years before I actually got to sew the badge on my sleeve. A very short time later I was drafted to another establishment.

It is not always considererd a desirable feature of life to be constantly on the move. But that was Navy life, and I looked forward to it. New experiences and new challenges stop me getting stuck in a particular curl of my brain, and a new move at that time was definitely what I needed. But that was coming towards the end of 1955, and Christmas was rapidly approaching, and I had to get through that before I was drafted.

CHAPTER 7

From the time that Pauline and I had split up, in 1955, I did my utmost to drive her out of my mind. I was doing pretty well, and had reached the stage where she no longer dominated my thinking. It wasn't easy, and every time I dated anyone else, I found myself thinking of Pauline. I would make comparisons; things would happen that brought her to mind. It would be a lot of years, I knew, before I would be over her, completely. Many times I wondered where she was, and what she was doing, and the view began to form in my mind that I would, one day, try and find her, or, at least, try and find out what had happened to her. When the time came, it came from a very unexpected source.

I don't actually remember when I made the first attempts to find Pauline. I do know that it was very tentative, and I was not seriously expecting to find her.

I don't think I even took the idea very seriously, at first, because, not only was it when Rosemary was alive, it was at her instigation. Yes, I know it seems ridiculous, but it really was Rosemary who suggested it. It was several years before she had dementia.

I do clearly remember what prompted it. It came from my sister, Elizabeth, who told me things, unwittingly, about Pauline that I had never known. Rosemary was there, and she asked me if that was the girl that I had told her about.

Rosemary and I had met just before Christmas, 1962. I say 'met', but we had seen each other quite a lot before we got together, because Rosemary worked as a part-time barmaid, in a pub that was popular with the Navy. I was stationed at the Royal Naval Air-station, Lossiemouth, and was a regular frequenter of that particular pub.

I had arrived at Lossiemouth a few months earlier, under quite bizarre circumstances. I had come to realise what a big gamble life was, but I had never conceived that my life could be changed, dramatically, by the drop of a card, literally, the Jack of Clubs.

It was in the Spring of 1962, and I had been stationed at HMS Ganges, in Suffolk, for my second time, after I had returned from serving on a small Destroyer in the Mediterranean. My time there was to be short-lived, when I was told that someone had to leave, and it was to be either me, or another member of staff, called Webster. He didn't want to go; he had his wife and children there, so that was not surprising. I wasn't keen to go, either, but we were told to sort it out between us.

My best mate, at that time, Geoff' suggested that the best way to settle it was for us to cut cards, but Webster did not like that idea, because he said it was a bit too abrupt. To prolong it, Geoff' suggested that he would deal out the cards from the deck, face up to each of us, and the one who got the last Jack out would go. For some crazy reason, Webster was satisfied with that, as a solution.

Geoff' dealt out the cards, in front of quite a crowd of excited onlookers. The first of the Jacks fell to me, the Jack of Hearts. The next two also fell to me, and excitement was mounting. Surely, by the law of averages, the final one was bound to fall to him. I learned, right there and then, never to trust to 'the law of averages.' The last one; the Jack of clubs, fell to me also.

A short time later, I was on my way, to Lossiemouth, and what was to prove the most life-changing move of my life. In less than a year I was married, and set on a course that I could never have dreamed of, before that card fell. (I kept that Jack of clubs, along with Pauline's letters, the fateful letter from her mother, and the one from my mother, for several years, until they were stolen, as I have said).

I hated Christmas, and had done since 1955, when I lost my home, and found myself in the wilderness. That particular Christmas, 1962, I had opted for the second leave period, which included the New Year, instead of Christmas, as I always did when I was stationed ashore, and I had nowhere to go anyway.

For some reason, that I can't recall, I had not made any attempt to find somewhere to go for my leave. I had received some offers of bed only accomodation, with married colleagues who lived in married quarters near the air station. I did, eventually, stay with one of them, in Elgin, but it was a last minute decision.

My very close friend, Alistair, had started dating a Wren not long before Christmas, and he had gone on leave with her to her home in Dorset. He actually met her through me, because Janet worked alongside me in the sick-bay; well, in the dental department in the sick-bay. She was a dental surgery assistant. Alistair was a seaman; a leading-seaman, and for a seaman he had a very strange job – he worked as an ostler, looking after the camp riding-stables. I rode regularly then, and that is how we became close friends.

He met Janet when he came to the sick-bay to visit me. Their relationship had become very serious, and I envisaged losing my drinking partner sometime in the very near future. I was also casually dating two Wrens, myself, and they had also gone home on leave, so I was feeling pretty lonely and miserable.

One evening, I decided to go out for a drink on my own, to find some company, really. The bar was a bit like a resort bar must be like in the winter. Normally very lively, it was practically empty and as quiet as a library reading room, but I did see a young airman that I knew, sitting with a girl. He asked me to join them, and introduced me to his girlfriend. A few drinks later, and feeling much more 'relaxed,' our conversation turned to why I was on my own, and his girlfriend suggested that I should go to the Christmas dance at the air-station. I said that it wasn't likely, as I had no-one to go with. Another couple of drinks, and I said that I was going to ask 'that barmaid' if she fancied going to the dance with me. They thought it was a great idea, and cheered me on up to the bar.

'There's a dance on in the camp on Saturday night,' I said, 'Do you fancy going with me?' She looked at me with utter disdain, and replied,

'I would not go to a dance with you, ever. Please go back to your friends, and stop bothering me.'

'O.K. I'll pick you up about half seven.'

'You won't, because you don't know where I live. I've told you, NO! Go back to your friends and forget about it.'

'Well, what did she say?' asked Dave, and his girlfriend, simultaneously.

'She said yes!'

'That's great,' they said, 'See, how could she resist?' and they looked over to the bar and smiled at Rosemary. (She must have thought it was an evening out for the feeble-minded). Although I didn't actually know her name at that point, it was not difficult to acquire. She gave them a very quizzical look. I easily got her address from a barmaid in one of the other bars in the place.

When I arrived at her house at half past seven, as promised, she didn't seem greatly surprised to see me. She did make a bit of a fuss, and made some attempt to close the door on me, but it seemed a bit half-hearted.

'I told you I did not want to go to a dance with you,' she said.

There followed a lengthy period of agitated banter, which upset her mother, who was trying to watch 'Z Cars,' and they had a giant dog, called Roger, who looked like a small camel, and who was doing all that sniffing stuff that dogs do, and was not helping me in any way. Rosemary's mother came to the door and asked what was going on, so to save any more aggravation, Rosemary capitulated.

'Alright, I'll come,' she said, 'but if I don't like it I'm coming straight home.'

(Her sister Margaret told me at the wedding that Rosemary knew I had found out her address, because the other barmaid told her. She also had her dress laid out on the bed, ready. I had failed to notice that her hair was done, and she had on her make-up ready to go out). The next few days were incredible, and looking back, it still takes my breath away at the pace that things happened.

We didn't exactly hit it off on that first date. She couldn't dance, so there wasn't an awful lot of point in being at a dance. However, sitting out the entire evening gave us a lot of time to talk, and as it was live music in those days, (It was 'Shane Fenton and the Fentones,' actually. Remember him? he later became that bloke with a black glove, and got famous for a song called, 'My Coo Ca Choo!'), we could actually hear each other. I liked her. She was honest and straightforward, and was not trying to put on any kind of image. We arranged to meet the following evening at her house, and we talked a lot more. (Her mother did not like me. She thought I was 'posh' English, and whenever I was at the house she would go off to another room to be out of my way. However, it was not long before Rosemary's mother and I became very close. I called her parents mum and dad, and they were like parents to me, and their passing, some years later, was a great blow to me).

I learned that Rosemary was about three and a half years older than me, and that she worked as a telephonist at the Elgin telephone exchange. Her barmaid job was just around two or three evenings a week, and was her contribution to supporting her family – father, mother, a sister and two brothers at home, as the family income was not great. (She was the oldest of the siblings, and she also had another sister, who was married, and living in Elgin). During the day, I was on duty at the sick-bay in the air-station, and Rosemary was working in Elgin.

There was very little going on in the air-station as the squadrons were all on leave, and the camp was being run by essential personnel only. I had the sick-bay almost to myself, with very little to do. I had a lot of time to think. All kinds of things were going through my mind.

Maybe it was because it was Christmas; maybe it was because every one I normally associated with was away at his or her home, with family, and kids, and all of the things associated with Christmas; I hadn't even had a Christmas card in the previous seven years, or sent one. I felt excluded. I wasn't old, but I was beginning to miss a life that I didn't have, and the future looked bleak. I had spent almost eight years, when I wasn't at sea or overseas, cajoling mates into taking me home on leave with them, or spending a miserable leave in some dingy service-men's hostel.

Alistair would probably be getting married to Janet sometime during the coming year, and his time in the Navy was coming to an end in a few month's time. (My time should also have ended, but when Alistair got engaged to Janet, I signed on for another five years, and since I had already added two years to my service several years earlier, that meant that I was now in for fourteen years altogether. I believed then that I would probably go on to complete twenty-one years, making it my career).

For the first time since my mother threw me out, I missed having a family. The life I was leading just could not go on; out drinking practically every night; casual dating, and having no feelings for anyone who was important or significant to me, and having no-one close who had any real feelings for me.

On our third date I asked Rosemary to marry me! I didn't plan it, it just happened when we had been out somewhere, and had arrived back at her house.

Remarkably, Rosemary didn't seem all that surprised. Maybe I had found a woman as crazy as I was, but, in truth, I think she thought that I was not being serious, because I soon found out that Rosemary was far from flippant.

'But I don't love you,' is what she did say, and I had to be honest, and tell her that it was very unlikely, that in three days, we could, either of us be in love, but I said that I thought that with time we could learn to love each other, because we both knew that we had become very close in just three days.

What I couldn't tell her was that I didn't really believe that there was any such thing as love. For many years I had believed that love was the invention of romantic writers and pedlars of greetings cards, and popular music writers.

I had genuinely come to believe, from experiences I had had over several years, that even if there were any such thing as love, women were incapable of it.

The reason I wanted to get married then was for a secure and happy family life in the future. (At least, that is how I have rationalised it since. I can't think of any other reason). I wanted the warmth of a family home; children, and a reason to go home on leave, with someone to go home to. Love didn't come into it. Right then it was just a word. Maybe it could gain some substance in the future, I'd no idea. What I did know was that if we did get married, it would be a commitment for life. I was prepared to spend the rest of my life with Rosemary, and I felt that it was entirely up to the two of us. If the relationship stayed sound, with respect, honour, and trust on both sides, we would make it work. At the very least we could become good friends.

Incredibly, we did come to love each other, and after surviving many testing times, our marriage lasted for forty-nine years.

At that stage, I don't think that Pauline had entered my thoughts, but it's a long time ago, so it is difficult to remember that far back. But it wasn't long before she was there, though.

After she said she didn't love me Rosemary and I had to consider just precisely what was happening, and do some serious talking.

'I am nearly twenty-seven, and you are older than me, so neither of us is in the first flush of youth,' I said to Rosemary.

'So, what you are saying is that we are past finding anyone else who'll have us?'

'No, what I am saying is that we are not a pair of daft, love-sick teenagers, pining for lovey-dovey romance. I really believe that what we have discovered between us could well blossom into something greater, with time. I am very fond of you, and I think – I hope, that you are fond of me.'

What came next was a bomb-shell, and knocked me back a bit.

'I am fond of you,' she said, 'but for the past year I have been in love with someone else. His name is Mick; he is a naval airman, and he is married.'

I was flabbergasted, but she went on to relate the whole episode to me. I am going to be brief – she had started having an affair with him when he was, unknown to her, engaged to a girl in Cornwall. His squadron had then been drafted down to Culdrose, in Cornwall, and he and his fiance got married. For a brief period he was back in Lossiemouth, and he and Rosemary took up where they had left off. He did tell her,then, that he was married. He had then gone back to Culdrose, and he and Rosemary were still communicating.

I asked her if she still loved him, and she said that she didn't think she did, but it would need our relationship to be really sound before she would commit herself to me. I was concerned that she was on 'the rebound,' and I did talk to her about that.

Since this was 'cards on the table' time, we decided that if we were seriously intending to get married, it was best that we should have at least a semblance of understanding each other. I told her about things from my past that I thought she should know; about several relationships, and most especially about Pauline.

Even though it had been eight years in the past, I still knew how important it had been to me. I told Rosemary that I had loved Pauline very dearly. She asked me if I still loved her. I told her that Pauline was still very much in my thoughts. 'We were engaged,' I told her, 'but she had an affair with someone else when I was away, so I dumped her. It hurt me very badly, and that and other experiences, destroyed any trust in women that I ever had. I vowed at the time that I would never get married. I have held to that vow for nearly eight years, which isn't bad, surely?'

'So why do you want to get married now?'

'I don't know. I didn't plan it or even think about it. It just happened. Maybe time is the healer that it is said to be. Now, I know that I want to marry you, and the sooner the better.'

'It seems strange that after that you are now in such a hurry to be married. I would have thought you would have wanted to have a long engagement, to be sure?'

'As I told you, I find it very difficult to place any trust in women now, and if we hang it out I fear that I would allow my prejudices to rule my judgement, and I would not go on with it.'

'So you don't trust me?'

'I don't trust my feelings. I can get very jealous, very easily, and I don't want to give myself the chance to start mistrusting you.'

'But I could be unfaithful to you when we are married,' she reasoned.

'You could, but I don't think you would. Being married is a big commitment, and at our age it is not one we are likely to enter into lightly. Pauline and I were very young, and I was not entirely blameless. I did not treat her well, and I know that she was not sure that she could trust me. I genuinely believe that when we are really committed to each other, we will trust each other.'

That wasn't entirely the end of it. Her brother, Peter, worked in the air-station in a civilian capacity, and she set him the secret task of finding out if I was married. He didn't do the 'secret' bit particularly well; he came to the sick bay and told me what he was to do, and just asked me if I was married.

Getting married, and the talk about Pauline set my mind working. I found myself wondering where Pauline was, and what she was doing. Did she get married to that man she had been having the affair with? I thought that I would like to see her right now, just to tell her that I was getting married. I still had that indescribable feeling inside me whenever I thought about her, and I knew that it would never go away. I still even believed that I would see her again, one day, because I wanted to.

When I got engaged to Pauline in 1955, I really felt that I was in love, and that she loved me. We had planned to get married in 1957, when I was twenty-one, and she was nineteen. We talked about our lives together; children; she wanted four. We were blissfully happy.

If she had gone ahead and married that bloke, after

she had made that phone-call to me, in September 1956, three days before she was to get married, I didn't think her marriage had the tiniest chance of success. If it had gone ahead in 1956, she was eighteen years old. A child! I really found it so difficult to believe that, after all the plans that we had made, she could go and do that. A year ahead of the time that she and I had planned to get married. It didn't make any sense.

All of that had been a long time in the past. I just hoped that not only was I much older, I was also much wiser.

When Alistair returned from his leave, I asked him to be my best man. He was staggered.

'Don't tell me you're marrying Nicki?' he asked, mentioning the more likely of the two Wrens I was dating.

'Nicki? No, of course not.' I then told him about Rosemary.

Nicki and Abby', still had to be told, and I guessed, correctly, that Nicki would not take it too well, but Abby thought it was fantastic, and wanted to come to the wedding.

Rosemary and I were married in St Gerardines Church, Lossiemouth, on February 16th, nine weeks after I had proposed to her.

I am not absolutely certain when the suggestion that I should try and find Pauline was first mooted. It was late two thousand and seven that Rosemary's dementia had been diagnosed, though she had been having problems for at least a year before that, so the year I learned about Pauline must have been millennium year. Yes, it was, I remember now, I had retired in 1999, and had bought a computer with the money I was presented with on my retirement. I planned that among the projects I intended embarking on would be a genealogy exercise, because Rosemary wanted to find out things about her family.

My sister, Elizabeth, was spending Christmas with us at our home in Fife. She had come up from Leicestershire, where she had lived for most of her life. It was clear from the look on her face that she realised that she probably shouldn't have said what she did, but she'd said it, and couldn't take it back.

We were all talking old family stuff, and reminiscing about our old school friends, and people we had known, in one of those relaxed post Christmas-dinner moods. Elizabeth was talking about old friends and acquaintances from our youth. I hadn't been to Leicestershire since my mother threw me out in 1955, except on the occasional visit to my mother after our reconciliation in 1972, so I was completely out of touch with any of my old friends and acquaintances'

'Pauline carried on writing to mum,and visiting her, you know, after you left her, right up until mum died,' revealed Elizabeth.

Obviously I knew which Pauline she was talking about, in spite of the feigned quizzical look on my face. It was also clear that Rosemary probably knew too, judging by the look on her face. Elizabeth saw both, and quickly tried to change the subject, but it was too late.

'Is that the girl you once told me about?' Rosemary asked.

'It probably was,' I said, 'It must have been.'... 'You mean the Pauline I was once engaged to?' I asked Elizabeth.

I tried to remain calm, and in control, but a ridiculous thrill was running through me, and I was desperately trying to put things into perspective in my mind. 'My mother died in 1993,' I was thinking. 'How old was Pauline, then?' I tried, in my confused mind, to work it out. 'She was born in 1938. That means that she was fifty-five years old.' I thought, surely she couldn't have been visiting my mother since she was seventeen?' I was reconciled with my mother in 1971, when she came to my graduation in Aberdeen, and that was the first time I had seen her since 1955. I had visited my mother, in Leicestershire, around two or three times a year since then. That meant that she and Pauline had been in communication for over twenty years during the time that I was visiting, and I knew nothing about it. My mother, and Elizabeth, had kept that secret all those years.

I was on a different planet, with my head in a turmoil, so I wasn't aware of what conversation was going on at that moment. My reverie was broken when I vaguely heard Rosemary saying…

'You should try and find out what happened to her, and where she is now.'

'Don't be daft. That stuff is all in the past. You don't go looking up old girlfriends. What's the point?'

'I just thought you would be curious, that's all. What did happen to her, Elizabeth?'

My dear sister, realising that she had to go on with the story said,

'I can't tell you very much, because she was really only involved with mum. She knew everything about you. She knew when you got married, when Gordon was born, when your grandchildren were born. I did see her when she visited mum, and I think, once, she actually had her husband with her, Lord knows what she told him about her visits, and I know that mum wrote to her quite regularly. She did visit me once, when I was living in Spencefield Lane. Her husband dropped her off at my house. She brought the two children with her, Alex and Sarah. I remember it particularly, because I had just rescued a sick budgie from somewhere, and nearly all its feathers had come out. I remember the two kids were completely fascinated with it. I think they thought I was a bit strange.'

'The two children?' I posed.

'Yes, she got married. She was very young, and I remember thinking that she was bonkers after what you did to her. It ended in divorce, but she had the two kids. I think she was living in Guildford, or somewhere down in the south-east. Mum used to say she spoke Cockney. I sent her stuff after mum died. Photographs, I think, of Pauline and the children with mum. I'm sorry, I can't remember where I sent them to.'

When Rosemary had suggested that I should try and find out what had happened to her, I dismissed it out of hand, but I knew that I would try. When I learned that Pauline had remained in touch with my mother all those years, I had to wonder why. I think I realised then that she must have loved me, and that she was seeing my mother to maintain some kind of contact with me. My mother's last letter to me, when she threw me out, had made it clear how distraught Pauline had been when I left her. I had ignored that. I had thought only of myself, and the guilt I had felt, once I was able to think rationally, became acute with that new information. How much I had hurt her, and the tears she had shed when I took back her engagement ring, loomed then in my mind.

I had always known that I would, one day, at least look for her. That feeling became a commitment, I think, at that moment. So Rosemary's suggestion set the wheels in motion, I suppose, but it would be a long time before anything fruitful was done.

CHAPTER 8

Nothing was done about finding Pauline, at the time Rosemary had suggested it, but I kept it at the back of my mind, nevertheless. I did get more information from Elizabeth, over time, and I began to connect things together, and began to realise that I may well have been terribly wrong to trust the information that Pauline's mother had fed me.

I agonised for some time, not only over whether I should try and find Pauline, but how, (if I did decide), to go about it. I had bought the computer about two months prior to that Christmas, but I hadn't a clue how to use it. I hated the thing, because it scared me, and it sat unused for about six weeks. I'd used one at school on odd occasions, but with a lot of help from computer literate colleagues.

Eventually, my son, Gordon, gave me some lessons, and I tentatively went on-line, experimentally messing about, and regularly messing up. I think it would be about the end of January, following 'revelation Christmas,' when my sister had revealed the details about Pauline's continued contact with my mother, that I first started tinkering with genealogy sites, and I mean tinkering, because not much was achieved. I was working on Rosemary's ancestry, and doing reasonably well, after a while.

Feeling that I was getting proficient enough to find things, I looked for Pauline. I started with her birth. With a name like 'Phizacklea', I thought, she shouldn't be too difficult to find. (I loved that name from the first moment I heard it. I told her later that when we got married she should retain it. 'Phizacklea-Spiers', I said. Imagine the doors that a name like that would open, we joked).

I found her birth; twenty-second of May, 1938, in Tamworth. Tamworth? I always thought she was born in Melton Mowbray, where her father had a farm, in the district of Scalford, and where she was living when I first met her.

I went no further. I was suddenly overwhelmed with guilt. What possible purpose could I have had for doing that? If I had found Pauline, then, what would I have done next? Apart from anything else, I was doing it in secret, and it was clear that I shouldn't be doing it, so I stopped right there.

Over a period of months, I did well with Rosemary's ancestry, as I became more and more adept on the computer. I even got back to the mid-eighteenth century. (Coincidently, Rosemary's ancestors also came from farming stock, and had never strayed from the North-East of Scotland).

Over a lot of years, I did, occasionally, take another dip into finding Pauline, but never finding out very much, or making a really serious effort, until around April/May 2012, about four or five months after Rosemary died.

Even though Rosemary was dead, I still felt very guilty about what I was doing, but I think I alleviated that by telling myself that I just wanted to know what had happened to Pauline, and anyway, Rosemary had suggested it.

At the same time I started looking for Alistair, my best man when I married Rosemary. It was quite probable that in my mind, looking for Alistair and Janet legitimized my search for Pauline. The last time I had seen him was in 1965, when I was about to leave the Navy to go to university. He and Janet were then living in Torquay. He was a policeman, then, and they had a baby daughter, named Anne. After that we lost touch, completely, and I really did want to know what had happened to them. (I found, and went to visit Alistair and Janet, on the Mull of Kintyre, before I found Pauline).

When I looked for Pauline, I wanted to find good news, but I wasn't sure what good news I actually wanted. Having found so very little in past forays, I went back to the beginning again – births. Definitely born in Tamworth, and with an older brother, Richard T. I had met Richard, once, in 1954. He was about a year older than Pauline, and he was on sick leave from the R.A.F., with a broken arm, sustained when he had fallen off his motor-bike. I found several Phizackleas, in and around Melton Mowbray, and wider Leicestershire, and I was able to trace some of them back to Richard, but when Pauline got married she became a 'Taylor,' and I soon discovered that around half the people in England seemed to owe their ancestry to 'those who made and repaired clothes'.

I had never really known whether or not Pauline had married when she said she was going to. About a year after we had parted, she had phoned me, in September 1956.

Following our split, in 1955, and after a very unsettled period in my life, I made a rather drastic move, and volunteered for active service. It was the equivalent to joining the French Foreign Legion, I suppose. My heroic death would make her very sorry for what she had done. Oh yes! That would teach her. It was 1956, and things were happening, and I had just finished my training at Deal, in Kent, when I was sent back to the hospital in Chatham, for a very brief period, because of a flu' epidemic, or something of the sort.

Having finished a long, and arduous shift on a ward, I went to the mess to relax with a beer, when I was called to the phone.

'Hello?' I enquired, grumpily.

'It's Pauline.'

I was startled, and not at all happy to receive the call, and I almost put the phone down on her, but I thought that I should hear her out. There were no preliminaries, like 'how are you?' I think she heard the hostility in my voice. She just said,

' I'm getting married in three days' time!' Silence!… 'I wanted to tell you.'

I felt such a mixture of emotions then. I was saddened; hurt; angry and jealous. All of these feelings and more. I thought 'she really has the gall to phone me and tell me that she is about to marry the man that she had an affair with behind my back. Why?'

'Really!…so why are you telling me this?'

'Tony, I want to see you. Please Tony, I really need to see you,' she pleaded.

Her voice was tailing off, and I knew that she was having difficulty speaking.

'You are about to get married and you want to see me? Are you inviting me to the wedding?' I replied, as cuttingly as I could. I was starting to feel confident, and cruel, and I intended pressing home my advantage. 'Or maybe you want me to send you a wedding present?'

'Tony, please don't. I don't want to get married Tony. I don't love him. I don't want to marry him,' she blurted out, in a rapid stream.

I could hear the tears in her voice now, and I could also tell that she didn't want me to hear them. 'Isn't it just a little bit late for that? You might have thought about it a year ago, when it was me you were supposed to be marrying. What's the problem, are you pregnant?'

'No! I'm not pregnant,' she shouted into the phone. 'How could you say that? That's a horrible thing to say. Why are you saying these things to me? I loved you Tony…I still love you.' There was no hiding the tears now, I could almost feel them coming out of the phone. 'Tony, if you will only see me I won't get married. I need to see you Tony, please. Please Tony, just see me so that we can talk. If I marry John it will be wrong; it will be wrong for him and for me. I'm only asking you just to see me.'

'Pauline, you are eighteen years old. You are a stupid child. Love! I don't think you know the meaning of the word. I have no idea why you have done this. I am not going to see you, that is over. You got yourself into this mess, so you can get yourself out of it.' I was angry then.

I hung up on her without another word. Then I cried. I got away from the phone and cried like I had never cried in my life.

Did she marry him? I could never admit it to her, but I cared. I really cared.

The evidence was there now, in front of me, and there was I, fifty-six years later, feeling hurt – her wedding to 'John H Taylor, bachelor, in Melton Mowbray, September, 1956.'

My sister had said that Pauline had moved to Guildford, or somewhere in the south-east, so I phoned Elizabeth to check it out.

'It's such a long time ago,' she said, 'I'll see if I can find anything to jog my memory.' She called me back to say that she hadn't found anything, but the more she thought about it, she was sure it was in Essex, and might have been Chelmsford.

I spent hours searching Guildford and Chelmsford. My computer skills were still very limited, and I just wasn't sure what I was doing. (I still have my hand-written notes from that time, and I can see that I was going over the same ground time and time again). Eventually Chelmsford came out on top when I found the birth of Sarah, in Chelmsford, but it still wasn't a certainty because I found the birth of 'that' Sarah's brother, Alexander, in Hemel Hempstead.

There was no trace of Pauline, though. There were plenty of Pauline, or P Taylors, but nothing which indicated that any of them was 'my' Pauline. Since I hadn't the slightest idea whether she was alive or dead, or whether she had remarried, I decided that I had to bite the bullet and search the records for deaths, and the ones for marriages. I know that it may sound really callous, but I would rather have found her dead, than remarried.

If she was dead, then that would be the end of it. There would be no need to go on, so I searched death records first. I went through painful agonies during those searches. Every time I came across a 'P. Taylor' my heart sank, but there was nothing found, that was of any relevance.

Death records turning up blank, I turned to marriage records. My little world turned upside down when I was certain that I had found her remarriage in Leicester. That was near enough to Melton Mowbray, and she might have returned to her roots.

It is impossible to describe how I felt, at that point. For weeks I had immersed myself in the work of trying to find Pauline. I had become animated; excited even, and it seemed to have come to an end in the worst possible way. But there just weren't enough details to make it conclusive. Through all of my tinkering, I discovered that if I paid a fee of one hundred and twenty pounds, I could find much more detail. I paid! Relief, the dates, and various other details were wrong. Thank heavens it wasn't her.

Having been able to discount remarriage and death, I returned to Chelmsford, and 192.com. One Sunday afternoon I spent hours phoning every P. Taylor in

Chelmsford that I could get a number for. Even though the exercise proved fruitless, I enjoyed the experience, because a lot of the people I spoke to wanted to know why I was looking for Pauline Taylor. I had some lovely conversations. Most people really do love a nice romantic story, and I made the day for a lot of people that Sunday.

Having achieved nothing with the phone-calls, I came back to the two children, though, of course, they weren't children any more. Alex, I had no success with at all. There were so many with that name that it was impossible to find him. Even with Sarah, it proved very difficult. I found two who could have been her, and I did several days' work on them, but I could not find anything that would positively identify her as the 'Sarah' I was looking for. In fact the only positive factor for both was a wedding in Chelmsford.

Back to the Phizackleas in Melton Mowbray, I went. Among them I found several who were very likely to be grandchildren of Richard, so I made the first foray into the 'real people' world by writing to them. I said that I believed that they may be the grandson/daughter of Richard T Phizacklea, who formerly lived in Melton Mowbray. I explained that I was trying to contact his sister, Pauline Mary Phizacklea, who was known, in the family, as Mary, although I always knew her as Pauline. I enclosed stamped addressed envelopes in the letters, and asked them if they would, kindly reply, even if they had no news. After two or three weeks, with not a single reply. I felt so miserably deflated.

Having made that first actual move to Find Pauline, I had let my imagination run wild, with all sorts of plans.

I had to face facts. There would be no replies, and I had to write it off as another failed venture. The best bet, however, was still to stick with the Phizacklea name – to find Richard.

It was at the end of May, 2012, that I found just one Richard T Phizacklea, in the whole of England. He was living in Northamptonshire, and that was well within the bounds of possibility. As far as I knew, Richard was Pauline's only sibling. From my research, it would seem that he had been married twice, and some, or maybe all, of those I had written to in Melton Mowbray were definitely his grandchildren. I did not want the disappointment of getting no reply from a letter again. This time I found a telephone number. I made a note of the number on a piece of paper and put it on the coffee table. I stared at it. I knew that this was going to be a voice contact, and that scared me.

I went over and over the resulting scenario of a call in my mind. Why is it that the natural propensity, in such circumstances, is always to think so negatively? It's like going to the doctor's with a lump. You hope you can just make it home again before you drop dead! What would I do if he said she was dead, or, ultimate disaster, remarried? I saw her happily playing with her grandchildren, in her cosy living-room, watched by her smiling husband. She could be in a nursing-home; she's seventy four now, and there are people in care homes at that age. How about severe health problems?

Even if none of those things applied, there was still the biggest probability that she wouldn't want to hear from me. I had treated her hideously in 1955, so I couldn't blame her, if that was the case. The phone-number sat on the coffee-table for days. I just didn't have the courage.

I decided that it was a stupid idea. It was a half-baked romantic dream. Being so close brought a life into the whole exercise that hadn't been there before. This was going to be the biggest move of all; the make or break move. The only reason I went on was because I was able to half convince myself, that all I wanted to do was to find out what had happened to her, and how she was.

I wrote down what I was going to say. I actually wrote a script. I crossed out words; I added words; I changed the words around, and I produced something that I thought would do. Then I rehearsed it, for God's sake, with the telephone in my hand! I practically learned the words. I imagined what Richard would say; what questions he would ask and how I would answer them. He would probably put the phone down, anyway, thinking I was selling double-glazing. In fact, he probably wouldn't pick the phone up, if he didn't recognise the caller. I had run out of excuses. I had to get on and do it, or forget it.

It was June 3rd 2012. A date that can never leave my mind. The phone rang at the other end; it was answered – 'Yes?' said a rather abrupt male voice. Not unfriendly, just a trifle irritated.

'Hello, is that Mr Phizacklea?' I could barely read my script because I was shaking so much, and my vision was blurred. I was in that limbo between dread and elation.

'Yes!' This time in the affirmative, rather than a

question, and possibly a little softer, as if he had realised that I wasn't trying to sell him double-glazing.

'Mr Phizacklea, my name is Glenn Spiers...you will probably think this a rather strange request, but I am trying to find someone whose name was Phizacklea, and who I last had contact with over fifty years ago... Her name was Pauline Mary Phizacklea, and she was living in Melton Mowbray back then. I know that she got married, so she would not have the same name now, of course... I know that she had a brother, Richard, who was about a year older than her.' There had been no response up to that point, so I presumed; hoped, he was still listening, and at least he hadn't hung up on me. 'So, simply, did you used to live in Melton Mowbray, and do you have a sister called Pauline Mary?' During the rehearsals of what I was going to say, I had drummed it into my head that I must say 'do you have a sister', and not, 'did you have'.

'What did you say your name is?' A hint of suspicion in his voice at this point.

'It's Glenn Spiers, but she always knew me as Tony, at that time.'

'I think I vaguely remember you...it's a long time ago...well, yes, I did live near Melton Mowbray, and I do have a sister named Pauline Mary.'

The adrenaline was pumping now; I was feeling drained. I was so weak that I just hoped I could go on.

'We did actually meet. Just once, I think. You were in the R.A.F. and you were at home with a broken arm. It was at 'Wolds Farm,' in Scalford, right?' I remembered Richard in his RAF uniform, with his arm in a sling, slightly built; a year younger than me. If I could have seen 'the Richard' on the other end of the phone as I was speaking to him then, I think I would have shrunk, and lost any confidence in my quest. (Pauline and I went to see Richard and his wife Vivienne, not long after we were married. It was nowhere near the Richard that I had known in the fifties. He was, now, thickset, 'country built,' I would say, with a beard shaggier than mine; taciturn, and although he and his father had never really seen eye to eye, Richard was prone to his father's abrupt pig-headedness. However, we got on OK and he was very friendly towards me).

'Yes, that's right. I do remember it. You got engaged to Mary, didn't you?'

The old familiar Leicestershire voice was obvious now, and it took me winging back over the years.

'Who is it?' asked a female voice in the background.

The phone was then, obviously, shielded a little, with that belief that the caller wouldn't hear.

'I'll tell you in a minute… You'll never believe it.'

He hadn't mentioned anything about her being married, or said anything about my enquiries being inappropriate, so I took this as a good sign.

'I do have your address, so if I send you a letter with Pauline's name on it, Taylor, isn't it? could you put her address on it and send it on to her please?'

'Yes, it is Taylor.' Thank God, I thought, at least there hasn't been a remarriage. 'That would be fine. Yes, I'll send it on to her. She'll certainly be surprised. I think she'll be pleased to hear from you, actually.'

Do you ever do those things with your hands when

you are on the phone, waving them about to emphasise things, as if the other person could see you? I was not only doing that, but I imagined that he could see me shaking, with a stupid, vapid grin across my face. He must have been able to detect the strain in my voice, surely, but, then, he wouldn't know that my normal voice is about two octaves lower, would he?

'Look, Mr Phizacklea, perhaps it might be a good idea to phone her first, to let her know that I have contacted you. I wouldn't want to give her a heart-attack. Also, she might not want to hear from me, and if that is the case, you could let me know. I'll put a letter in with it for you, with my contact details in it.'

'Yes, that's probably a good idea. I shouldn't worry, I'm sure Mary will be really pleased to hear from you.' There was a note of real enthusiasm in his voice now, as if he knew that he was being involved in something special.

'Thank's Mr Phizacklea, I really do appreciate this.'

I put my head back and closed my eyes, utterly drained. I had tinnitus; a dry mouth; a swollen tongue; a sweaty skin and my eyeballs were hurting. I felt as if I was going down with malaria, or something. But most of all I felt elated. 'She'd be really pleased to hear from you,' he'd said. God, I hoped so.

I went out for a walk, to clear my head. Although it was early June, the temperature was a bit down, so it was a jacket day. There were occasional appearances of the sun, but it was generally a bit cloudy, but at least it was dry. I remember looking at the flower beds on my way up the drive, and thinking how neglected they looked. Rosemary would not have been happy with the way I had neglected things that year. Normally, I would have prepared and planted a completely new bed during the Spring, but I had not had the slightest inclination to put in any effort since Rosemary had died. The beds weren't even weeded.

I could see people working in the fields. For the first time since I had lost Rosemary, I was beginning to feel reconnected again. It was less than six months, and, in spite of the work I had been doing to find Pauline, I had still had that feeling of being locked in a cupboard, away from daylight.

It was good that I had got this far in my search, and I was experiencing an expectant thrill, but I had also been hit by a contra-feeling of 'downness'. I was exhausted. I had put so much emotional effort into finding Pauline. At that point there seemed to be a natural break, before I went on to the next phase. I had achieved something positive, and I was desperately hoping that the next move would not involve pain. I'd had enough.

When I got back into the house I got straight down to writing the letter to Pauline. The walk had refreshed me. I didn't even make myself a cup of coffee, as I would normally have done. As I sat at my desk, I pictured her in front of me, and wrote as if I was talking to her. I tried to age her, but she was still seventeen years old, and wearing the same skirt and blouse that she wore when I last saw her. I even saw the tears in her green eyes as she looked at me. I headed the letter with four different contact details. Apart from my address I included my email address, phone number and mobile number. It was hand-written.

Dear Pauline,

I hope your brother, Richard, forewarned you, or this letter may be a bit of a shock, assuming that you remember who I am. It is difficult to know what to say after such a long time. 'Hi, how have things been for the last fifty-seven years?' doesn't seem to do it. I do want to ask you so many things and to tell you things, but a letter is not the place. I would like to see you, or talk to you properly. I do get down to England occasionally. In fact I was there three months ago to see my sister Elizabeth, who lives in Norfolk now. It was Elizabeth who told me, only recently, that you kept in touch with my mother. She also told me that you had two children, Alex and Sarah, but that your marriage had broken down. I became reconciled with my mother at the beginning of the 70's, but she never told me that she was in touch with you. In fact, she never ever mentioned you. We did not ever relate closely, but I visited her occasionally. I am very close to my sister now. I really don't want to put things I want to say in this letter. If I could phone you and talk to you it would be better, and maybe sometime we could meet. It has taken some time to find you, and when I phoned Richard he seemed to remember my name. I only hope you do, but I'm not sure if you knew me as Tony, or the name I have used for well over fifty years, Glenn. I sincerely hope you do not mind me contacting you; I've wanted to do it for a long time, but could

never decide whether or not you would want to
hear from me. I hope we can talk soon.
  Fondest wishes,
  Glenn (Spiers)

Yes, Pauline kept the letter, along with every other letter she ever got from me, plus all Christmas and birthday cards, in a giant, heart-shaped chocolate box, that she had received from me, and that is it, word for word.

Of all the contact details I had put on the letter, I really hoped that she would phone me. I wanted to hear her voice.

You know, it's remarkable, but that was the first draft of the letter. I did not edit or rewrite it in any way. I next wrote a short letter to Richard, on the computer this time, not hand-written. The personal touch was not important with his letter.

I sealed the letter to Pauline in an envelope just addressed to Pauline M Taylor. I almost wrote Phizacklea! I put it, with the letter to Richard in an envelope, and addressed it; stuck the stamp on and then sat staring at it. I felt a sense of relief, but there was also a mixture of fear, anticipation, longing and excitement. How, in the name of heaven, had I, at the age of seventy six, put myself through this?

It was June 3rd , a Sunday, so the letter would not go that day, but I decided to go out and post it right away, to stop me staring at it, mulling over it and worrying about it. Also, that meant it would go first post in the morning.

For the next few, impatient, days I would live through her moment of getting the phone-call from Richard. I saw the look on her face. I lived through her excited anticipation of the letter and saw her face when she opened it and read it. Strangely, all of her reactions, in my vision, were exactly the same as mine except that she was a seventeen year-old septuagenarian, not an old thing, like me. Yes, I was arrogant enough to believe that she would react to it all just as I was doing.

In my mind, I calculated the logistics. The letter would go on Monday 4th, so Richard would get it on Tuesday. He only had to put her address on the envelope and post it. (Naturally, I imagined that he would rush out immediately and post it on), so she could get it on Wednesday. Just in case there are delays, though, it might not get to her until Thursday. Pauline could ring me on Thursday, probably in the evening.

I began to wonder how I would answer the phone when it rang. I knew that I had to be sure not to become 'adrenaline drunk.' Adrenaline could be the most wonderful life-saving friend, in so many circumstances, but I had painful memories of times when it had been my worst enemy, turning me into an incoherent, gibbering idiot. I recalled times, sitting in interviews, knowingly saying things that I just did not either think or believe, and being unable to do anything, other than make things worse by uttering even more stupidity. Times when I had so looked forward to meeting someone that I greatly admired, and when the time came, blurting out some unbelievable banality.

Rehearsing the imagined conversation, I waited.

It was a long week. In spite of my logistical calculations, I really wanted her to phone me on the Wednesday. But she didn't. Nor Thursday. Nothing on Friday saw me sinking deeper into despondency. Clearly, she didn't want to be in touch. Maybe something I'd said in the letter had upset her. I am stupid to think that all was going to be a rosy ride into resurrected romance. The warm glow of a new dawn was starting to chill. I was dejected.

In fact, Pauline didn't get the letter until Saturday morning.

It was Saturday, June 9th.

When I saw the number on the caller ID, I knew it was her because, after my Sunday of phone-calls around Chelmsford, the dialling code was branded on my memory.

'It's Pauline!'

The adrenaline was pumping. Control! Breathe slowly. Think before you speak. It was not the voice I had been expecting. It was clear, confident, even friendly, and a strange accent. The last 'Pauline voice' I had heard was quiet, a little timid and naïve. It had had love in it. This voice had 'friend' in it. No matter, it was her. Nearly six decades of my life rolled back. Although I had worked so hard to get to this moment, I don't think that I really believed it would come. How I answered, I have no recollection whatsoever, except that there were tears and trembling and fear; from me, not her.

'I never, ever forgot you, Tony.'

CHAPTER 9

I have begun my life again so many times in my long existence that I am well able to recognise when it is happening again, and a new chapter has opened. I think I have always been aware when I am setting out on a new path, sometimes more aware of the importance of some new direction than of others, and when I heard that voice on the other end of the phone, I was very aware that this could be the rebirth above all rebirths. When I heard –

'It's Pauline,'

on the ninth of June, 2012. it was a voice so different to what I was expecting, and I think I knew that the life I had planned, and lived in my imagination for months was not going to be. It is said that a new war is always started where the last one left off. I was certainly not expecting a war, but I had definitely been hoping that love and war had those similarities, and in my imagination our new life had begun where we had left off in 1955. But it wasn't going to happen that way, and from just the sound of those two words, I knew that here was a different scenario.

Back in the 1950's, I think I was, what most men are, without thinking about it, a bully, when it came to women. I don't mean that I physically abused Pauline; I didn't shout at her or threaten her, or set out to bully her; I just took it for granted that I was in charge; that the relationship revolved around me and what I wanted.

Pauline had been so young, I don't mean just young in years, but she was a naïve child in everything about her. In the guilt that I have carried around with me, for over sixty years now; yes, it is still there, I have had to come to terms with the fact that I took terrible advantage of her. It was the fifties, and people did not behave then as they do now. I was wrong to make love to Pauline then, a child. When I bullied her on the phone that September, in 1956, as she humiliated herself, in a desperate plea for help, I knew that I was breaking her heart again, just as I had done a year earlier.

In my dreams, since I had sent that letter off to Richard, I had looked in on the conversation we would have on the phone, like an out of body experience. I had heard us make plans until we met, and fell into each others arms, all kisses and tears, and the plans we would make for our wedding, before a life of bliss together. She would be the devoted Pauline that I had known, with her pretty head on my shoulders, while I made plans for us – consulting her, of course. I am a new man, after all – and I think I saw her being as submissive as she had been the last time.

I know that I said I had convinced myself that all I had wanted was to find out what had happened to Pauline, but when I look back on it, I am pretty sure I was lying to myself. Whether I was believing myself, I'm not so sure.

Those first two words put me right. Her voice was friendly, but firm, and it said, 'the world has changed' my friend. It had, and I was soon to find out by how much.

We were on the phone for over two hours. We talked about so much of our teen years, of the wonderful times we had had together, and I formed new pictures in my mind of this new Pauline. I saw her sitting comfortably in an armchair, feet tucked under her and brushing her hair from her eyes and her smiling, friendly face. Her hands moved, as did mine when describing things, and warmth flowed from her. What she remembered amazed me. There were things that we both remembered so colourfully; events that Pauline recalled, that I could not remember, and vice versa. I saw the room she was in. It was so light and airy, and very tastefully decorated, with flowers in vases. But most of all I could see her face and her body, and I embraced her fondly. Very early in the conversation, after I had told her how the guilt of what I did still haunted me she said,

'Please Glenn,' she had started to call me Glenn from the beginning of the conversation, 'when I found out about my mother's letter – your mother told me about it – I forgave you. It made me understand why you did what you did, please don't feel guilty.'

'You didn't know about your mother's letter, when you phoned me, just before your wedding, did you?' I asked her.

'No, it was about two years after you and I broke up that your mother told me,' Pauline replied, 'I carried on seeing her, and writing to her, and she was so good to me, Glenn. I don't think I would have got through it without her. You really broke my heart, Glenn, and I couldn't talk to my mother. Your mother was like my 'real' mother to me. I think she thought I was pregnant when I first went to her, and she, and your sister, Elizabeth, said that they would look after me. I only wish she had told me right at the beginning about the letter. My mother wrote to her, as well, did you know that?'

'No, I didn't know that. Have you any idea what was in the letter?'

'No, your mother didn't tell me, but I think she answered it. She didn't tell me what she had said, either, but she said it had been pretty forthright. Your mother didn't tell me why you had left home, either, but she told me that she was able to keep in touch with wherever you were. She knew that you had changed your name, and she always knew all about you. I don't know how, but it meant that I was always able to keep close to you.'

'I never did find out how she knew those things. Even Elizabeth had no idea.'

'When she told me that you had become involved in politics, I used to try and find things out about you. I watched out for you on the TV anytime there was anything on about your Party, and I even looked up your election result in the paper, and I was really disappointed that you didn't get elected.'

'That's incredible, because I used to wonder if you ever

saw any of my interviews, or read any of my Press, but I don't think any of it ever appeared outside Scotland.'

'She told me when you got married, and that did hit me very hard. Up to then, I think I had always kept the hope alive that we would, one day get back to each other. I knew it was a stupid dream, but it just kept me going. After you got married, the bottom dropped out of my world. I felt so empty, and I didn't go to see your mother again for a long time. When I did go back, I think she knew why I hadn't been to see her for so long, but she didn't say.'

The phone-call on that Saturday went on for two hours, and we spent another two hours on the phone the following day, Sunday 10th. A lot of what we talked about was just reminiscing, and we shared remembered, fond memories, but we also learned things that we had not known, and one of those revelations dug deep.

'Pauline, although I appreciate your forgiveness for what I did, I can't let myself off the hook so easily. Since it happened all those years ago, I have had to evaluate what I did, and to recognise how wrong I was. I have never even thought of it as trying to forgive myself. I wanted to learn something positive from my actions, and for many years I have done my best to treat people with a lot more respect, and to understand that there are more people in the world than me. What you did, hurt me deeply, and I did blame you for a long time, but you had good reason. I was treating you abominably.' There was a moment's silence before Pauline replied.

'But I didn't do anything, Tony, I honestly didn't do anything wrong.'

When she reverted to the name, 'Tony', I knew that she had been shocked by what I'd said, and I felt the anxiety in her voice. 'What about John? You were seeing John when I was away?'

'I wasn't seeing John, or anybody else. I never cheated on you, Glenn. I hung about with a bunch of kids that I knew in Melton, boys and girls, but they all knew about you, and there was never anything between me and anyone else, ever. I thought you knew.'

'No, I didn't know. How could I have known, there was no-one to tell me. But when you phoned me to tell me that you were getting married, I just presumed that John was the one you had been having an affair with behind my back. You married him a year after you and I parted, so how long had you known him?'

'Glenn, I started going with him about three months after you dumped me. I was bereft, Glenn, I was devastated when you dumped me, because I didn't know why. I thought you had met someone else. You used to tease me about all the nurses and Wrens that you knew, just to wind me up, but you were really hurting me, and I felt that you just weren't serious about me. I had a friend called 'Bobby', and she knew how much I loved you, and how hurt I was. Since I spent all my time crying, it wasn't difficult. She took me to the pictures, but the picture was 'The Cain Mutiny'. All I could see was naval uniforms, and I howled all the way through it. Eventually, she got me to join the badminton club where we worked. John was a member, and although I saw him there, it was months before we even spoke. He offered me a lift home one night, and when we were talking I told him about you, and what had happened to us. He was sympathetic, and kind, and I was vulnerable. I know it was a rebound, I even knew it at the time. It was even me who bulldozed him into marriage, although, as you know, I also knew it was a mistake. I went through with it because I thought I could make it work.'

There was a very long pause before I was able to speak…

'Why didn't you tell me this when you phoned me? Did anyone else know how you felt?'

'My mother knew, because I told her, but she wouldn't take it seriously. She said it was just nerves, and that all brides get nerves on their wedding day. But I knew it wasn't nerves. I thought about telling your mother, but I didn't. I wish I had now. When I phoned you I wanted to ask you why you had dumped me, but I was scared that you would say it was because you didn't love me. I didn't know that you thought I was cheating on you… All these years you have thought that?… Even when you got in touch, now, you were still thinking that I had been seeing someone behind your back?'

I was struggling so much with what I was hearing. I had always blamed myself, but I had never known just how much I had been to blame.

'Yes, Pauline, I have always thought that you were seeing someone else. Even if it wasn't John, I genuinely believed that there was someone.'

As I was learning the truth of what had happened, fifty seven years previously, I felt sick, but there was still one thing that I had to know. Pauline had promised to tell me, but she never did, and I had not asked her at the time.

'When we split there was something wrong between us. Things were happening that I couldn't understand, and I started doubting you. Your mother's letter just confirmed my fears. Pauline, there was that weekend, the one before I saw you for the last time. You said you would…'

'The Sunday I didn't come to your house?'

'Yes, Pauline. You promised that you would tell me why, but you never did.'

'I was scared to tell you, Glenn, because you told me, once, that if my dad ever hit me you would leave me.'

'So, he hit you?'

'Yes. It was after my mother had read your letters. There was a blazing row, and they told me that I wasn't to see you any more, and they made me go to my room, and not to leave it. That was the Sunday I was supposed to be with you.'

'So you couldn't get out of the house…Obviously, you couldn't phone me either. God, I'm so sorry Pauline.'

'I climbed out of the window of my bedroom, and got my bike, and went into Melton and got on the bus. While I was waiting for the bus to leave, my dad's car pulled up alongside the bus. I saw him, and I couldn't do anything about it. He got on the bus, and he dragged me off and threw me into the car. When we got back home, he dragged me into the barn, and he thrashed me.'

At that stage, the tears were coming, from both of us, and I just couldn't speak.

'I was seventeen years old, Glenn. Could you imagine any parent doing that now?'

'But you came to me the following day, the Monday, how did you manage that?'

'I went into Melton, as usual, to go to work, but I didn't go. I got the bus to see you, instead of going in to work. Unfortunately, one of the girls from my office saw me getting on the bus, and reported me. When I went in the next day, I was sent for, and I got the sack.'

'All these years I have thought you were seeing someone else. But I got you thrashed, I got you the sack, and then I dumped you. I just wish, to God, that you had told me Pauline.'

'I couldn't, Glenn, I was so scared that you would dump me. You had said you would.'

'I don't know what I would have done, Pauline. It's too long ago to think about what I could have done.'

'Glenn, I loved you so much I would never, ever have even thought of going with someone else. I lived for every moment we were together. I desperately looked forward to every leave; every long-weekend we would be together. You were my whole life. I loved you so much. I have always loved you, Glenn. I never stopped loving you. Over all these years I have so often thought of you. You weren't in my mind always; just now and then something would remind me of that time, and you would be there. Sometimes I needed you there, and I conjured you into my mind… What made you get in touch with me again? You must have forgiven me for what you thought I'd done?'

'Why did I get in touch? We will need a lot longer

conversation to explore that, Pauline. When we split, I was, at first, angry. With the years I have had a lot of time to go through many different emotions. I never thought of it as forgiving you, because I felt that that would be arrogant; it would imply that you were wrong and I was right, and that was never how it was. I knew that I was, at least, equally to blame, for so many reasons… Right now I am stunned… I feel like the worst person on earth… I stole fifty-seven years out of our lives… I can only say that I have done my utmost to learn from what I did. That one year when we were just children had a massive impact on my life, Pauline. I don't think I learned anything, to start with, and I went on to hurt someone else almost straight after we split, and the worst of it was, I did it on purpose. It took me a long time to change my life; to stop hurting people; to understand that blame is never one-sided. I never think about forgiveness at all. It is never in my power to forgive, because I'm not perfect. The only time it ever comes into the equation is in regard to myself. I know that, even though you have said you forgive me for what I did, I will never forgive myself.' There was a long pause before she replied…

'Hello, are you still there?' I asked.

'Yes. I know what you mean, but I never forgave my parents for what they did. Your mother was keeping me well informed, and I told my parents everything about you, just to rub it in. 'Tony's been promoted to Petty Officer;' 'Tony's at university;' 'Tony's a teacher now;' 'Tony's standing for Parliament.' They were never allowed to forget what they'd done. I think my dad realised that they shouldn't have done what they did, but my mother never showed any remorse. The awful irony is that she lived until she was ninety two, and I was left to look after her for years after dad died, and she became even more hateful to me as she got older. Even though I travelled miles, and spent hours looking after her, she cut me completely out of her Will. If my brothers hadn't shared what they received with me I would have got nothing. I didn't want her money, but I would have liked a little appreciation.'

'I'm so sorry it turned out like that for you, Pauline. If you and I had been married, those things would never have happened to you, so now I feel that I subjected you to even more hurt than I could ever have known about.'

'Why they were so against me, I could never understand, but I felt that your mother was perfectly justified in what she said to me. She was being a protective mother. That's why I believed her, because many of the things she said were true.'

'No Glenn, she was not being protective, she was just being vindictive. They thought that you weren't good enough for me; just a common sailor. They were snobs; always were. If they had left us alone we might have run our course, anyway, and split up our way. I don't think so, because I genuinely believe that we were in love. I know we were very young, but if it hadn't been love why are you contacting me now, and why do I still feel like I do? One thing it definitely taught me was to never interfere in the lives of my kids like that, and I never did. They made mistakes, of course they did, but they could always come to me and talk about things. There were no secrets, and no condemnations.'

'After what you did I went to your mother; I had no-one else to turn to, and your mother was a better mother to me than my own mother ever was.'

'We all have an agenda, Pauline, and my mother was so fond of you because she saw you as a fine 'Catholic' girl, who would straighten me out. I didn't get on with her, but because of what she did for you I feel much better disposed to her. I am glad of that; pleased that I can have much more positive memories of her. I do sincerely regret the way in which I judged her, and the way I treated her. I had no right to do that. People were right – the war years were different – and humanity was subjected to a complete reversal of what was considered normal behaviour. Morality was turned on its head. War does that. It isn't normal, so how can people behave normally?'

We spoke about a lot of things in those first two phone-calls, but what we learned the most about our past, I wanted you to know, because it hit me very hard. But, I think, our calls always ended on the river bank in Melton Mowbray!

That news that Pauline was completely innocent of the infidelity that I had judged her guilty of set my emotions in turmoil. I had added up all the parts of the situation, and come to entirely the wrong conclusion.

I thought of the hundreds of incidents throughout history when some historical 'accident' had altered the course of the future. The 'trampled butterfly' of the past. Some battle or other that was lost because the commander had toothache – wasn't it Napoleon? Some other battle was influenced because someone couldn't ride his horse because his piles were playing up, and there was the infamous 'Charge of The Light Brigade', led so valiantly by Errol Flynn, in the first movie that Pauline and I went to see, when the 'Chinese whispers' of command mixed up the message that sent hundreds of men to their deaths.

I told Pauline that I had tried to learn from those mistakes I made in the past, but that was not strictly true. What I had tried to do was to treat people better, and to understand that everyone has feelings, which is not really learning from the past. As a historian, with half my degree in history, I think that I have learned that the only thing we can learn from history is that history teaches us nothing! But this revelation was my 'personal' history, not something out of a book of fabrications. It was me who had to come to terms with it, and it was not easy.

On Sunday 10th June I printed off some photographs of myself and Rosemary, and sent them off to Pauline, with a short note. I still have that note and the pictures, and I had said that I was looking forward to seeing her on July 15th, so I must have made arrangements to go and see her pretty quickly, on either that first or second telephone conversation. I said how much I was looking forward to seeing her, and I hoped that she was, equally, looking forward to seeing me.

After that weekend I was filled with all those feelings that you get after something, long-awaited, has come and passed. I was elated and deflated, enervated and enlivened, exhausted and exhilerated. A hundred different futures were alive in me, and what glowed most within me was the feeling I had got from the calls, that Pauline was so friendly, and close.

We talked, lovingly, of those days together. We talked frankly and lovingly of the most memorable times we had spent wrapped in each other's company. We laughed about the first time together in the cinema; we both remembered so much detail of things that happened and of places we went. Some things I remembered that she didn't, and vice versa. Pauline remembered the very first time we made love, which, to my shame, I did not remember, until she triggered it, and then I remembered it vividly.

Our youth returned to us in those calls. She asked me about Rosemary, because it was only when I told her, in the first call, that Rosemary had died. I was still very raw after losing Rosemary, and she was silent as I wept through the last moments of Rosemary's life. The loss of someone you have loved dearly, and spent so much of your life with, turns you inside out, and makes you the only person left on earth, and it just didn't occur to me what I was doing to Pauline as I told her things about my marriage to Rosemary. My self-absorption was tearing her apart, and I was inflicting deep wounds. I was certainly to learn about it later, but as I spoke to her, Pauline was deeply sympathetic.

As the week progressed I settled more to my life as it was, and came out of my dreams. We had agreed to speak on the phone again the following Sunday, and in the meantime I had a normal life to live.

The weather was good that week, and I pottered about a lot in the garden, and there was always shopping to do. These things brought my feet back to earth.

Tuesday June 12th I wrote Pauline quite a long letter. I expanded on things that we had talked about on the phone. I had told her, on the phone, that my mother disowned me because of what I had done to Pauline, because Pauline didn't know. She had said that she wondered why I was never at home, but my mother did not enlighten her, and it came as a shock. I was able to quote some of what my mother had said in her letter from memory. On the Friday, the 15th. I received an email from Pauline to say that she had got the photographs I had sent her.

'Haven't got any that I can send to you,' she wrote, 'not easy to take photos of myself! You will have to wait until you see me, so I might come as a bit of a shock!'

I replied right away – 'Sorry I look so old, but I don't have any choice about it. I'll bring my camera with me when I come to see you. In the meantime I'll make do with my imagination. If you are too hideous I'll just keep my eyes closed a lot.' Pauline's email had just ended, 'Bye for now, Pauline,' but I decided to end mine, 'Love, Glenn,' and to give it two kisses.

I received another email that evening, reminding me that she was just two years younger than me. She also, rather abruptly I thought, thanked me for the letter, but she did end her email, 'Love, Pauline,' but with just one kiss. I was to learn later that some things I said in the letter hadn't gone down well. (I read over it again just now as I'm writing this, and I can see her point).

Sunday June 17th was our next phone-call day, and it was also my sister's birthday. I had sent Elizabeth a card, but I also phoned her. I told her in that call that I had found Pauline, and that we had spoken on the phone. She was pleased, but she was puzzled. She didn't say so, but I could tell by the tone of her voice. I said very little about it, though. I would tell her more if there became more to tell.

It was also Father's Day, so Gordon rang me later in the evening. After I had spoken to Pauline, actually. When I told him about Pauline, I described her as 'a new girl-friend'. He was really delighted. He had been in constant touch with me for a long time, since his mother got dementia, because he knew the strain I was under, and he felt very guilty about living so far away, and unable to give me some practical help.

He was living with his partner, Lili, (a beautiful French/Caribbean lady from Guadaloupe), in South London. I gave him a brief account of who Pauline was and how I had rediscovered her. He was amazed, and absolutely delighted, but he did tell me not to go overboard, because it had been a long time, and we hadn't seen each other yet. When I told him that she lived in Essex, he said,

'Essex! Are you sure about this, dad?'

'Behave yourself, toe-rag. Show more respect to your wise and aged father. And don't forget some of the places that you have resided in.'

Not long after we had hung up, the phone rang again, and it was Gordon on the ID, but it was actually Lili, and she was excited to the point of hysteria. In her fabulous French accent she gushed at me,

'You 'ave met your first girl-frien' again, Glenn? That's marvellous; that is so nice. Is she beautiful? She must be beautiful. This is so good. When do you see her?' She said a lot more, and I was able to say something now and then too, but not much.

This, as I said, was June 17th and I emailed Pauline around mid-morning to remind her that I would be phoning her in the evening, and I asked her what time she went to bed. Pauline hadn't had her laptop very long, and wasn't too adept in it's use, and I would just like to quote one bit from it when she replied about an hour later –

'I go to bed when I'm tied.'

I'll leave you to imagine what went through my mind as I smiled at that. She said that Sarah would be on the phone for about an hour, from 8 pm, so would I call after that. Reading through her email brought it home to me that we were running out of things to talk about. She spoke mostly of the weather; pottering in the garden; her arthritic hands, and all the kinds of trivial things that you normally just see on 'Facebook'.

The evening phone-call was a little better, but the pauses were getting longer, the sighs deeper, and I began to see that we had exhausted our repetoire. There was a limit to the things that could bear repetition, and I think we were on the verge of it. I said so to her, but obviously not too well as she replied,

'I'm sorry if I'm boring you!'

'That's not what I said. I was trying to say that I can't wait until the middle of July before I see you; I want to see you sooner.' Long pause with no reply. 'If you can put me up for two or three days, can I come down next week?'

'July seemed OK to me, but if that's what you want I've got a spare bedroom, so you'd be welcome to stay.'

Her tone had changed, and I should have taken heed. I blustered on, however, and I said that I would see what flights were available from Edinburgh to Stansted, and I would phone her back as soon as I had done that. I really should have been more instinctive, because that was the last email communication between us for exactly a month. I was on the verge of ending our fairytale story very prematurely.

Maybe I was moving things on too quickly. I should definitely have talked the idea over with her more fully before I bulldozed ahead, but I went on and found a flight. I booked a flight for Thursday, June 21st and we agreed that I would stay for three nights. I did it because I wanted, so much to see her, and, as so often, going against the prevailing wind, and failing completely to read the situation as it was.

I parked the car at Edinburgh Airport, and sat around waiting to board the plane. I was so expectantly excited, fidgety and anxious. My mind was rehearsing the meeting, and I was trying to picture her, and her reaction.

I looked at the people around me and I wanted to tell them where I was going, and why. Like the hand-holding child in the queue who looks up to you and says 'we're going to Disney World'. That was me. An excited child going somewhere unknown.

Throughout the short flight I read the flight magazine, bearing pictures of Edinburgh and London. I even read purile articles advising me how to get the best out of something or other, or informing me of something I'd always wanted to know about some celebrity or other that

I had never heard of. I just twitched my way throughout the whole flight, restless and hyper.

At Stansted I found my way to the bus to Chelmsford and boarded. The last leg. I had just a small bag with me and I kept it on my knee, drumming my fingers on it.

The day was a bit overcast, but warm. I watched the Essex countryside rolling by, looking, I think for something reassuring. Occasionally I would catch a signpost indicating the mileage to Chelmsford and my heart would give a little leap, and as we got closer I began to question the wisdom of what I was doing.

By the time the bus got to Chelmsford I was ready to leap onto a bus back to the airport, and put the whole experience down to stupidity. The bus pulled in to the little bus-station. Pauline knew what time I would be arriving and had agreed to meet me off the bus. There was another short bus-journey to where she lived.

She wasn't there. I looked around. There were some people on the stance, but none looked as if it might be Pauline. I walked around, past the standing buses and tried to imagine what I was actually looking for. I had sent her pictures of me, so she would know who she was looking for.

After about five minutes I was beginning to feel quite down, and very lonely. England seemed huge, and all around me now, and I was lost. After another circuit of the bus-station, I had just arrived back at my starting point when I heard the voice behind me.

'Glenn?'

CHAPTER 10

Since I had left home that morning I had been in such a state of euphoria. I had become a client in one of my own autogenic, controlled breathing exercises, on a fantasy journey through the air. I had been on that fantasy journey as I drove down to Edinburgh; as I sat in the departure lounge and during the flight. It was so important, during the relaxation exercise, that the ending was comforting, positive and left a great feeling of well-being in the participant, or the exercise would be wholly counter-productive, leaving a person deflated, and dangerously anxious, and troubled. I was on the verge of that bad ending. I could just feel it happening as I looked into her face.

'Pauline?'

I wanted to say something, but my mouth and brain had both seized up simultaneously. My bag was on the ground so I reached out to her with both hands to give her a hug, but her hands came up to hold me off and she instinctively turned her face away from me as if she was expecting me to kiss her. I saw the mood more than I saw the vision. There was total silence between us as she turned away from me and began to walk. I picked up my bag. I was in a place that I didn't like, seriously frightened of what was happening.

'This is our bus,' she indicated, and we boarded.

'I'll get the fares,' I said.

'I have a bus-pass,' she replied, producing it and showing it to the driver, who nodded his head at her before he looked enquiringly at me. I think he expected me to produce a pass too, but I knew that Scottish bus passes don't apply in England.

'How much to…?' I turned to Pauline. She told him the destination.

'Three pounds fifty, mate.' I took change out of my pocket; not enough. I reached for my wallet in the inside pocket of my jacket. I could feel the impatience of those boarding behind me. 'Why can't people have their money ready!' was the look I was getting.

Pauline was already in a seat, looking out of the window and paying no attention to what was happening to me, clearly not wanting to share my discomfort. I handed the driver a Scottish ten pound note. He looked at it, and then at me. I gave him an apologetic look and he rubbed the note between his fingers, then held it up to the light. Other people were looking at it too, and at me. None of it said 'welcome'. With a sigh the driver opened a metal cash box and placed the note inside. Not with the others, but in a separate bit, obviously not wanting to contaminate his other notes. With a rattle, my change hit the tray, (no five pound note), he pressed a button and with a whirr my ticket appeared and he pointed to it, knowing that as a Scot I wouldn't know what it was. He sighed again and looked past me at the next passenger, expectantly. I picked up my bag and moved into the bus and sat down next to Pauline.

Silence! She still looked out of the window. For the first time I tried to take in what she looked like. She was old. She looked severe. Her hair was silver, like mine, but I already knew it would be because she had told me. It was 'man-short;' much shorter than mine, and steel-grey seemed a very appropriate description of it at that very cold, hard moment. She was slim, but I knew that also, having been told. I couldn't see her face properly because she was still looking out of the window. During our phone calls she had told me,

'I remember that you have dark brown eyes, and I remember that your birthday is January 27th. I always look at your horoscope in the paper. Funny, I always have done. Do you remember the colour of my eyes, and my birthday?'

'You have blue eyes, and your birthday is in June.'

'Well done! I have green eyes, and my birthday is May 22nd,' she had laughed.

God, how I would love some of that friendly banter now, I thought.

'How long is the journey?' I ventured.

'Not far!'

'Right... OK'

When we reached the destination, she looked at me without speaking and started to move, indicating that we were there, and should move into the aisle to get off the bus. It was a short walk to her house through a pedestrian way between houses. All of the houses looked pleasant; two-storied and were built in terraced blocks. It was a heavily populated area, very different to my little stone-built farm cottage in the middle of nowhere. Her house was mid-terrace, and we entered it through a tall back-gate, which led into a very pretty, well-kept little garden, filled with blooming flowers; perennials, I noticed, cottage-garden style – roses and blue geraniums predominating. As we reached the back door I could hear a plaintive mewling coming from the other side of the door.

'Alright Maisie, I'm coming,' said Pauline. My heart gave a little drop further. I am not comfortable with cats! When Pauline unlocked the back door and opened it a tortoisehell cat darted between our legs and disappeared into the flower bed. I shuddered, as we entered the kitchen.

'She's been with me for fourteen years, since I retired,' explained Pauline, 'my only companion,' she said, pointedly, 'she was a rescue cat that I got from a rescue centre when she was a kitten.' (Later, Maisie and I became inseparable friends. An absolute miracle). Going through to the living-room, Pauline turned to me and spoke real words of proper communication for the first time.

'Well, what do you think of my little house?'

'It's not so little, and it's lovely,' I said as we stood in the spacious living-room. Then just to make sure that she hadn't intended to sound friendly she said,

'I don't really know why you've come. You're going to be bored out of your mind.'

She took me upstairs to show me the room I would be in. It was a big room, and very comfortable looking, but that was the only place there was any comfort at that moment. Downstairs again Pauline asked me if I'd like a coffee, and I replied,

'Yes please, black with no sugar please.'

'Sit down.' To my questioning look she said, 'any place you want, just please yourself.'

There were two equal sized settees; a matching pair, and I sat at the end of one while she went into the kitchen to make the coffee. Coming back with two mugs she said,

'could you sit in the other one, I prefer this one,' and she placed the two mugs on a pair of coasters on a coffee table, handy for both settees. The significance of us not both sitting on the same settee was not lost on me.

'I have tea in the afternoon,' she said.

There was such a barrier between us, and it seemed that at every turn she was determined to put something in to make it wider, and came up contrary to everything I said or did.

'What made you go and live in Scotland?' she asked.

'I was posted there in 1962,' I replied, 'to the Royal Naval Airstation at Lossiemouth. When I got married I decided that I would like to stay up there, because I liked it. When I left the Navy I went to Aberdeen University.'

'I don't like Scotland!...' 'I stayed with my sister Dorothy near Perth once. It was too cold and too isolated for me. I'm a city girl through and through. I like plenty of shops, and lots of people around. I hate the country.'

'I live in an old stone farm cottage, miles from anywhere, I'm afraid.'

'I know, your mother told me, and you sent me a picture of it. She didn't like it either.'

'But you were a farmer's daughter, and Scalford was way out in the country. We had some lovely walks around there when we were going together.'

'That's probably why I hate the country. I couldn't wait to get away from there. I think that's why I married so young, to get away, and John lived in Watford.'

After we had finished our coffee and tea, Pauline sat back on the settee and curled her legs beneath her, and leaning on the arm of the settee picked up a book and started to read, after putting on a pair of reading glasses.

'You can watch the TV if you want,' she said as she looked up at me as if suddenly remembering I was there. She left the settee to turn on the television. 'Anything particular you want to watch?'

'No, anything at all. I don't watch much TV,' I replied, 'so I've no idea what's on.'

'I'm practically a TV addict,' she said.

I've no recollection at all about what programme was showing. I didn't watch it. My mind was full of plenty of other pictures at that time, and I think I was trying to find something there that would be worth watching. I couldn't hear the television, anyway, because she had the volume turned almost to inaudible, because the neighbours lived only a few inches away through the wall, as she explained.

'There's a paper over there,' she said, 'If you want something to read.'

I had already noticed the copy of a popular tabloid on the lower shelf of the coffee-table, which did not bode well, since that is a publication I would not handle, even to throw in the bin, without wearing very thick oven-gloves. (Thank God I was to learn later that Pauline was quite political, and her politics and that 'rag' were light years apart. For some reason or other, thousands of people read that thing who are not in the slightest bit of its persuasion. Pauline told me later that she only took it for its TV guide).

The silence ticked on. I looked out of the window to the front of the house. She had a small patch of lawn, that terminated at a public footpath, at the other side of which was a straggly hedge, and then a view into the end of a road which was a part of a new-looking housing development.

'When I first came here thirty two years ago, all that out there was a sportsfield, with tennis courts and pitches and stuff,' Pauline said, noticing me looking out. 'It was really nice. It belonged to Ferranti, but they sold it to a developer, and that's what happened to it. It's dreadful now. Full of all sorts of undesirables. In that house there,' she pointed, 'there was a drug dealer. The school kids from the school over the way come along here on their way to school, and I used to see him selling them drugs from my bedroom window.'

'Is he still there?'

'No! In the early hours of one morning, just a couple of weeks ago, I woke up to an almighty racket going on outside there. I looked out of the window and there were about four police cars, with flashing lights going, smashing their way into the guy's house. They dragged him out half-naked, and handcuffed. He was yelling obscenities, and kicking and struggling.'

'I presume he didn't return?'

'No, but his case hasn't come up yet. In that house there, across the road from the dealer, there used to be an old man; retired. Two or three days after the bloke was arrested, some thugs broke down the old man's door, and they beat him almost to death, and slashed him with a razor. He's in a critical condition and still in hospital. Apparently, they thought that he had 'grassed' on the dealer. Everyone knew that it wasn't him, though, because the police had been watching that house for ages, from inside someone else's house.'

I had difficulty hearing this, and I was trembling. I think I must have turned white. I felt as if I had. 'This is awful, Pauline, doesn't it frighten you?'

'Not really. You just have to get used to that sort of thing here. It's maybe not as bad as it sounds, and now he's gone it should be a lot better. Problem is that's a house where they tend to put problem cases.'

'You can't get used to that Pauline, I shudder to think what might happen to you, living here.'

'Well I don't want to leave here, I like it here, and I've got friends. I'm not going to last much longer, anyway.'

I was startled when she said that, because I had no idea what she was talking about.

'What do you mean, you're not going to last much

longer, you're only seventy four, two years younger than me. Remember?'

'I've got rheumatoid arthritis; it just came on about four years ago, so it isn't really bad, but the last time I saw the specialist he told me that it had caused me to get pulmonary fibrosis. My lungs are shot. I reckon I've got about two years left. I'll probably be in a wheelchair before then, with an oxygen cylinder attached.'

I couldn't take this. I stood up and walked to the other end of the room and looked out of the back window onto the garden. I was still very delicate after losing Rosemary. It had only been six months. I know that reconnecting with Pauline had helped me through it, but I was still grieving. My legs were shaking and I felt the tears coming, and as they started to course down my face I reached into my pocket for my handkerchief. A weakness was drifting over me. I am an emotional person, anyway, and tend to shoot from the tearducts, but this was making a bad day completely unbearable.

'Please don't say that, Pauline, Please. You are exaggerating, aren't you?'

'God, you're much too emotional for me. I can't stand all that weepy stuff. I don't have emotions any more, I'm the 'ice-queen'. I'm not that shy little creature that you used to know. I've had over fifty years of 'real' life to knock all that out of me. What's it to you anyway? You've no need to be bothered about what happens to me.'

'I am bothered about what happens to you, Pauline. You have always meant a lot to me, and even though we haven't seen each other for fifty seven years, I have still kept you in my memories, and in my heart.'

'I doubt it. You weren't concerned very much about my welfare when we were together, so I can't see how you can say that I meant a lot to you.'

'Anyway, I always have a liedown in the afternoon, so I'm off to my bed. You do whatever you want.'

Normal service had been resumed. I sat back down on the settee, staring into space. I felt sick; miserable; lonely; outcast, and I wanted to go home. I had taken an emotional beating that had floored me, and I was glad that she had gone out of my sight.

It was about two hours later that I heard Pauline stirring upstairs, and going into the bathroom. My head was in a mist; some kind of suspended animation. My relationship to my immediate environment was detached. I couldn't tell you anything about that two hours that Pauline slept, because I just wasn't there, and I've no idea where I was.

'I'm going to make dinner, how do you like your steak?'

'What?'

'Dinner; steak; how do you want it cooked?'

'Sorry. I like mine rare please.'

'Do you mean rare, as with the blood running out of it, or do you really mean medium?'

'No. I mean yes, I like it really rare.' The blood was running out of me, because by the tone of her voice I knew that I was in for more.

Fillet steak! What woman, on a pension, gives fillet steak to a man that she so obviously detests? The sounds from the kitchen were cooking sounds, only, no conversation. I tried.

'Can I do anything to help?'

There was no reply, so I took that as a 'keep out of my way.'

'There you are, there's yours. I hope it's how you like it. I couldn't eat anything like that. I'm almost a vegetarian. Sit there. Help yourself to wine. It's South African, is that OK for you?'

Fillet steak and wine? I just could not get my head round all these mixed messages. What on earth was going on, I had no idea, but I wasn't expecting a truce anytime soon. And none came.

'Yes, that's fine,' I replied, and I sat down to my meal. It looked so good, but I wasn't sure that I had an appetite, but I knew that appetite or no, I would eat every morsel.

'What kind of wine do you usually drink?' She asked me.

What response I would get to my answer was wholly predictable, but I answered.

'I like most wines, but I suppose I usually drink French wine, I enjoy a Burgundy or Rhone wine, mostly, but I also like a Claret. A decent Rioja is very nice too…I have spent a lot of time in Spain.'

'I can't stand French wines! They're full of tannin, and I think I know my wines!'

'This is a lovely meal.' It was, and I enjoyed it very much, but I felt a bit like John Major and his 'peas' when I said it. There just wasn't any conversation to be had. As I started to rise from the table I looked at her and was about to ask if I could help with the dishes, but she anticipated me and said,

'No. Just sit down. I'll go and do the dishes. Do you want coffee?'

'Yes please,' and I sat back on my 'scolding seat' and waited.

There was the angry rattle and clatter of dishes and cutlery from the kitchen, and the opening and closing of cupboard doors, then,

'No Maisie, you're not getting any more. You've had your dinner.' Even the poor cat seemed to be getting it in the neck for my sins. But then,

'That's all you're getting.' Reprieve for Maisie. Things were looking up. But they weren't. Maisie slunk into the living-room first, licking her lips, and looking straight through me with total indifference. She lay down next to the coffee-table and went to sleep. I was ready to join her. Good thing, puss, I thought, I wish I could switch the world off like that. Pauline came through and sat in her place. She sighed and opened her book.

Of all the Burns' Suppers I have been to in my life I have never seen anyone play the home-waiting wife from 'Tam o' Shanter,' like Pauline played her at that moment –

'Whare sits our sulky sullen dame,

Gathering her brows like gathering storm,

Nursing her wrath to keep it warm.'

I felt the 'wrath' of fifty seven years strike me as she slowly closed the book and looked at me.

'Why did you do it?' she snapped at me.

The unexpectedness of it startled me, and I felt my

mind stutteringly trying to work out what she was asking.

I fidgeted; looked at the floor; shuffled my feet; looked up in the air; gulped, then breathed in and replied,

'I genuinely believed you were going with someone else behind my back, Pauline, I'm sorry. I know now how wrong I was but at the time I was so consumed with jealousy that I didn't attempt to reason.'

'What?… Not that, I mean the letter. The letter you sent me. Why did you send that letter?'

There was a menace in her voice at that point, and although she was sitting half facing me, I felt it between my shoulder blades, like a cyclist in front of a London taxi.

'I'm sorry, I thought you meant… sorry, I just felt that I could say more in a letter, that's all. I didn't mean to upset you by it.'

'For God's sake stop saying sorry, because you aren't sorry at all. You certainly did say more in your letter alright. I think I just about shared every minute of your marriage to Rosemary. It was seared into me how much you loved her. I think I travelled with you on every journey you made together; the great successes of your educational achievements, and your wonderful careers, together. Even her illnesses have become a part of me, now. Have you the slightest idea what you did to me?' Then, as a parent answers the question to a child, 'why did you do it?' with the already known answer, 'I'll tell you why.' Pauline laid into me with, 'You are, and always were completely thoughtless. You haven't the slightest concern for anyone's feelings but your own, have you?'

I suppose I should have answered, 'no, you're right,

that's true,' but it wasn't true, and although I was drained of courage, I had to try and reason, somehow. 'You asked me to tell you, Pauline. You said you wanted to know.'

'I did want to know. I wanted to try and understand what sort of life you had led that should have been mine too. I didn't want to know about every pimple and wart. I didn't really want to know your feelings. It was something I wanted to try and share with you, not get assaulted with. We had been getting along so well, and then that. Why the hell did you come here?'

Before I had a chance to reply, Pauline got to her feet.

'It's getting late. I'm going to bed. You don't have to. You can do as you please. I've left towels for you on your bed.'

It was only 7.30 in the evening. There were still soundless pictures moving on the television, which had been on continuously since we had arrived at the house; Maisie was still sleeping by the side of the coffee-table, and it was still very light outside.

I sat for a while, then got up and walked over to the window and looked out. A man was getting into his car across in the new housing development. I wondered if he was going off to sell some drugs. A dog scuttled along the pavement; sniffed around a bush then lifted its leg. As a teenager came along wearing headphones and playing an air-guitar, I decided that I should cut my losses and leave. I wanted to go home.

I dragged my leaden legs slowly up the stairs. My small red weekend bag lay on the bed, unopened. I pushed it to one side and sat on the side of the bed. Ridiculously, I noticed how comfortable the bed felt. I lay back with my clasped hands beneath the back of my head and stared up at the ceiling. My eyes were stinging but trying not to cry. I thought back to December and Rosemary dying in my arms in that hospital in Dundee.

I went over the times I had searched for Pauline, and how we had been for the last two weeks on the phone and in emails. I knew that what had happened was my fault. It always is. I am selfish. I always have been.

I went through the dreadful guilt I felt when Rosemary died, because I killed her. I relived through the time I had told the doctors not to resuscitate her if she was not going to have a decent quality of life. Again I questioned my motives for doing that. Was it really for her sake or for mine? The tears really started to flow then, and I had to sit up because they were dripping onto the bed.

I heard Maisie padding up the stairs, and she pushed at the door and came in to the bedroom. She looked, quite startled, at me; stood, undecided for a moment or two, then turned and left. I noticed then the depression in the centre of the bed. 'Sorry, Maisie. I didn't mean to disrupt your life too.'

I had to think about how I was to get home. My return flight was booked for Sunday, and this was only Thursday. As I looked out of the window I could see the narrow pedestrian way that we had come along from the bus-stop. I remembered that there was a small shop opposite the bus-stop. I could ask in there about buses to Chelmsford, and I would easily find the bus to Stansted, and I was pretty sure I would get a return ticket alright. The problem was that it was beginning to get too late then. It had been quite a long journey from the airport to Chelmsford, so the chances were that I wouldn't get a flight to Edinburgh until the following day.

There was no energy left in me. I was thoroughly drained, and I didn't think I would make it to the airport, I really didn't. I decided that I would go in the morning.

If a villain is wrongly convicted and punished for a crime that he did not commit, and at a later date we are made aware of his innocence, then it is common practice to say 'well, he deserved it anyway, because he's guilty of other things that he probably got away with.'

It makes us feel better for the wrong we have done, and we believe it excuses us. I fully believed that I was innocent of the 'crimes' I was currently being punished for, but I had been a 'villain' in the past, so I deserved this, and, perversely, it made me feel better to see it that way. The damage I had done all those years ago was now being punished. Perhaps this was atonement, at last.

I was tired, but not sleepy. I freshened up in the bathroom, and I went to bed. It was a king-size bed, and probably one of the most comfortable beds I had ever been in. I half lay and half sat up, and I studied the room. There was a large wardrobe in a recess on my left, and on my right was the window that looked out into the car-park. There were three pictures on the walls; one a colourful abstract, another was a small original oil of a rural scene, and the third was a water-colour of a flower, like the plates that you see in glossy botanical books. It had the name of the flower italicised below it, and the name of the artist. It was a print. There was no chance of sleeping, so I got out of bed and went to the window.

Resting my arms on the window-sill I looked out into the street, with the cars parked alongside it, all bathed in the orange glow of the street-lights. Nothing was moving, not even a cat, and all looked so peaceful and quiet. It was a pleasant night. It may have been starry, but the light pollution made it impossible to see. The whole scene had a calming effect, like watching fish swimming around in a large tank.

I began to wonder what had happened. For some odd reason, counsellor that I am, I did not even consider it as her defence mechanism, but I was certainly forced to consider it later. At that particular moment it seemed to me that I was the one who needed to be defended.

When I had first arrived at the bus-station, and she had defended herself from what she thought was a coming hug, I think she said, 'slow down.' Contemplating this I drifted into so many places where this could have been said to me. I do go at things 'full ahead both engines,' I know, and so often I have to slow down to let the world catch up.

I went into full pictorial mode as I recalled the times when I had leapt into action; consulting no-one, and expecting everyone to just go along with me. Most of the time, once someone had been able to apply the brakes, a good end would come to it.

I needed to get my head out of there, to somewhere pleasant, and my thoughts just wandered. I went on holidays, with Rosemary and Gordon; camping in the mountains, as we had done so many times when Gordon was very small.

I travelled America, with Rosemary's youngest brother, now dead, and with my granddaughter, and my youngest grandson, as we had done so many times.

The familiar warmth of those happy memories was reviving my spirits. I did remember things that weren't so pleasant; times when my impetuosity had taken me very close to disaster, but I managed to keep Pauline out of sight for a short while.

I grinned my way through those pleasant reflections, and managed to dismiss the less pleasant ones, without inflicting any damage, but I was in Pauline's house, and I still had that to deal with.

I had to connect with Pauline, in some way or other, even though I had decided to go home, as soon as I could get away.

Although, any ridiculous ideas of romance that I might have had were well and truly dead, for the sake of my pride, I suppose, I had to slow down; to think before I did or said things, and recognise that most people in the world did things at a more leisurely pace. I did not like Pauline. She was not, in any way the 'Pauline' I had known fifty seven years previously, or the one I had known on the phone over the previous two weeks.

I stood at the window for hours, just going, stream of consciousness, over whatever happened to pop up. I had needed to get my head out of there, to be anywhere but in that house. At least I became more relaxed about what was happening. It was a case of accepting what was, now, instead of what I wanted it to be. I had not been in control of the situation in any way, because I had not been expecting It. In the morning, I thought, I would at least be ready for it.

The bed looked inviting, and I was very stiff, so I got in and pulled up the duvet. It was beginning to get light outside, and as I tried to sleep I began to wonder what time life began in Pauline's house.

For what was left of the night, I still slept very little. When you go to someone's house to stay, you always have to make the morning decision – do I try and get up early and get to the bathroom first, or will I wait until after the host has been in? I think I usually decide to go in after the host, so that was how it was to be. Luckily my bedroom was next to the bathroom, and I heard Pauline go in; the shower running and the bathroom being vacated. Pauline was an early riser. I waited until I thought she was out of the bathroom for good, and not just going into her bedroom for something, and then in I went.

As I unpacked my toileteries I discovered that I had forgotten my shower gel. This was going to necessitate our first communication of the day. Pauline had gone downstairs, I heard her go. Pushing the bathroom door open a little I shouted to her down the stairs to ask if she had a shower gel that I could borrow.

'No problem,' she shouted back, 'there is a tea-tree body wash on the shower rack that you can use.' Her voice held none of the menace that it had held before we went to bed. I heaved a sigh of relief.

'Thanks.'

Pauline actually half-smiled at me as I walked into the kitchen. 'What do you like for breakfast?' she asked.

'I just have cereal, usually. I never miss breakfast, but I don't really like a cooked breakfast.'

'Orange juice?'

'Yes please.' The tension was out of the air. It was cordial, rather than friendly. I felt hugely relieved. I just hoped that it would stay that way, but I still felt I was walking on eggshells.

That day was Friday, June 22nd. It was a none-day at the time, and is now, in my memory. We related as two strangers telling each other things. Though the things were of a kind that we both related to, neither of us seemed able to acknowledge the fact that we were talking about 'us'.

The two of us sat and talked a lot about the passing fifty-seven years; what we'd done; places I had been in the Navy; jobs she had done before returning to nursing. A lot of what we discussed went over old ground that we had covered before on the phone, but with a difference in the personal contact. The best I can say is that the day 'wore on.' I was well fed, I know, but I can't remember what we ate.

Pauline had her afternoon nap, as usual, but instead of going up to bed she stretched out on the settee, covered herself with a rug, and slept there.

In the evening, as I sat staring at the moving pictures on the barely audible TV, I felt like I did when I used to go into the hospital to visit Rosemary, at a time of one of the numerous occasions when she had been admitted. I would dutifully arrive at the beginning of visiting time. She would always be asleep when I went in, and open her eyes as I got a chair from somewhere to sit by her bed. I would hold her hand. It always had a big needle stuck in the back of it, with a tube dripping some liquid into her, and surrounded by purple/red bruising from the numerous attempts that had been made before a vein was found. Conversation, quickly exhausted, she would fall asleep again, and her face would turn away from me on the pillow.

I would sit throughout the rest of visiting time, looking at the clock, aware of every tick, and guiltily wishing the time away. I would never leave before visiting time ended. I had a duty to be there until the end. As I rose to leave when the time came her eyes would open; she would look up at me, and then close them again. I often wonder what she saw at those times, because she would have no idea who I was. Pauline looked at me with those eyes. She had no idea who I was.

As I stared at her sleeping form, stretched out on the settee, and thought about the bleak two days we had just spent together, I could not help contrasting what was happening there, with the times when I gazed on her beautiful body, in my bed, back in 1955.

Please God, if you really are all things loving, transport us back to then.

CHAPTER 11

I f you are being beaten on the head with a hammer, and even if you think you know the reason why you are being beaten, it does not lessen the pain. If you are being beaten on the head with a hammer, and you feel that you deserve to be beaten, it is still damn painful, and you would like it to stop. I desperately wanted it to stop.

I think I said to you earlier that this could be my atonement. I must qualify that now, and tell you that I believe no more in atonement than I do in forgiveness. Both, as far as I am concerned, are wasted concepts. I don't want to repeat myself, but I think that if you have committed an evil act, then saying sorry, being forgiven or making amends for it at some later date, does not take away the evil act.

I know that I said that I carried the guilt of what I did to Pauline with me all of my life, but that is not really accurate, either, because guilt is also a pointless state. It cannot solve anything, atone for anything or change what was done, in any way. What, I hope, I had carried with me throughout those years was a constant awareness of my wickedness to Pauline all those years ago, and a genuine determination never to do it again to anyone else. Pauline's suffering could never be erased, but I could, at least, become a better person. Pauline asked me once, not long before we got married, if I was marrying her to atone for what I had done then, and I told her, 'no. I'm marrying you because I love you. My feelings about what I did to you in 1955, were probably a big factor in why I contacted you again. I have always wanted to know what happened to you, but I can never make up for what I did.'

In any case, I was wrong in my evaluation. Pauline's punishment of me had nothing to do with what I thought it did.

If I thought that I had been beaten on the head with a hammer before, what was to come would make it look like a gentle tap with a ruler.

Friday, June 22nd, had been a comparatively quiet day, even if distant, but Saturday, June 23rd, the day before I went home, was a renewal of hostilities. Inadvertantly, I fired the first shot.

'You will be glad to see me gone, tomorrow,' I said. I was having a standing breakfast in the kitchen, while Pauline was doing something at the sink.

She turned to face me, eye to eye, and the look on her face said 'stand by for an attack.'

'I don't know why you came in the first place,' she said. 'I didn't invite you.'

'From the phone-calls we had shared over the last couple of weeks, I got the impression that you would be pleased to see me, and it would be nice to talk over the past times face to face. I felt that we were friends, and could cement some kind of contact and keep in touch.'

'Glenn, I don't think you thought any such thing. Your wife had died, you were on your own, and you just thought, "I know what I'll do, I'll contact one of the reserves." Was I the first one, or were there others before me who got the pleasure of your attention?'

'Stop. That's enough, Pauline. That was a hideous thing to say, even by the standards you've set yourself over this last few days.'

It wasn't a scene from 'Eastenders.' I didn't shout or threaten, or stamp my feet. I maintained a quiet, measured, tone.

'I'm out of here. I've, seriously, had enough. I need some air.'

What she had said was a huge blow, and I had to get out of there to clear my head and decide on my next move. I went into the hall cupboard and got out my jacket, and I said, 'I'm going for a walk. Is there anywhere around here for walking?'

'No, this is a town, not your open countryside, so you'll just have to walk around the streets,' she said, keeping her back to me.

(I discovered later that there was a park about three hundred yards from the house, but I didn't find it on that occasion). We were in Great Baddow, and I followed the signs to the city centre, and walked around Chelmsford. It was a pleasant day, and once the fuzziness was out of my head I was able to just think about my surroundings, and look at what I was seeing. I had to drive the bad thoughts away, and I managed it quite well. Chelmsford has quite a nice town centre; I window shopped; walked through shopping malls; had a coffee, and sat for a while on a bench by the river.

I didn't want to go back to the house, but I had to. By the time I got back to Great Baddow, I had been away over two hours. The tension returned, as I walked back, increasing with every yard. When I got to the house, I could feel the back of my eyes beginning to sting.

Pauline was upstairs doing something, I could hear her moving about. It is so ridiculous, but I felt a reprieve. I sat in my usual place, on the settee. The television wasn't on, for a change, so I had only Maisie for company, as she lay sleeping by the side of the coffee table. She had looked up at me when I had entered the living-room, but seeing nothing worth looking at, she had closed her eyes again.

Closing my eyes, I tried to compose myself. I was desperately hoping that I could gain some strength to stand up for myself. Pauline had seen how weak, and vulnerable I was, and I knew she would take full advantage of that, but I'd really reached the end, and had no intention of taking any more. God, how I wanted to go home, and put this nightmare behind me.

I heard her footsteps on the stairs, and immediately tensed up again.

'Where did you go?' She called through from the kitchen, where she had gone to put things in the washing machine.

'I walked into town, and had a walk round there.' There was no reply. If there was any thought in my head that my 'walk-out' had had any effect on her, it was soon dispelled. She came into the living-room, and stood with her hand on the table in the dining area. Looking straight at me, or even through me, she said,

'You did come here with some crazy idea that I was just going to fall into your arms, didn't you? Your idea was that I had spent the last forty-odd years just pining for you, and you would just walk in and sweep me off my feet!'

The heat had rushed into my face. I wasn't angry, I was just hurt, and hurt badly. 'No, Pauline, I didn't. I…'

'What we had when we were kids; and we were kids, was just play. It was 'kiddie love.' It was nothing special, or memorable. You thought, in your arrogance, "poor girl, what a terrible life she had because I dumped her". Well I didn't. I had a bloody marvellous life. You thought you were something special. That you could never be replaced. Well, I'm sorry, but you were way down the league table. After my divorce, a girl that I worked with said, "you don't want to get married again. Just have boyfriends, it's much more fun," so I did. I had plenty of boyfriends, whenever I wanted them. They knew me at work as 'the merry widow.' I just dated whoever I wanted whenever I wanted. As free as a bird.'

She saw exactly what it was doing to me, and she increased the pace, and she was in full flow. It floored me.

I knew what she was doing, of course I did, but it didn't make it any easier to bear. It seemed to go on for ages. I couldn't stand it.

'That's it, Pauline, that's it. I've had enough. I'm not taking any more. It was a stupid idea to come here, and, my God, I seriously wish that I hadn't, but I'm not listening to you any longer.'

This time I did raise my voice, and she felt the sting of it and took a step away from me. I jumped to my feet, grabbed my jacket, and stormed to the front door.

'Glenn!'

She spoke my name with an upward, quizzical inflection, a little panicky. I hesitated. I turned to face her. There was a strange, passive fear in her eyes. Not a frightened of violence 'fear.' Not a running away 'fear.' It was a deep down inside 'fear.' I turned away; opened the door and left. I had to get away as far as I could from that place. I have been in some very unpleasant, even dangerous, situations in my life, but nothing, absolutely nothing could compare to that.

I walked briskly back into Chelmsford, and I stayed there until the evening. I had a snack in some small cafe, and I wandered around. Lost.

It wasn't late evening when I went back to the house. There was still plenty of daylight left. As I walked back, I was too drained to think much about even the following ten minutes. I went straight up to my bedroom when I got back to the house. I saw Pauline in the living-room, leafing through a newspaper, as I passed. There was no comment.

It was my last evening there. I had to say goodbye, and

make some effort to get through to her. Why, I don't know, but I felt that it could not be left like that.

The daylight was still coming in through the window, between the curtains, when I went back down the stairs. I was very calm.

I crossed the room and sat beside her on 'her' settee, and I looked at her. I entreated,

'Pauline, I don't want to go away from here leaving things as they are. Why are you doing this, Pauline? Why are you treating me like this?' She had leaned as far back as she could into the back of the settee, to get herself away from me, and she looked at me and said,

'You just need to know, Glenn, that whatever was in your head, I'm not available.'

'I've tried, Pauline, heaven knows I've tried, but that's it. I mean that… is… it. Goodnight.'

I don't know whether or not she said goodnight in reply. I wasn't listening. For some strange reason I slept very soundly that night, and I was up in the morning before Pauline. I showered and dressed, and went downstairs. I was feeling remarkably calm. After what had happened already, nothing she could do or say could hurt me more. The torture was nearly over, and I was on the verge of release.

Since it was Sunday, the bus service was more limited than on a weekday, and, to get to Stansted in plenty of time, I would need to get a bus into Chelmsford at about ten o'clock. I was downstairs in the kitchen before Pauline, and I was preparing my own breakfast before she arrived.

She said nothing, and completely ignored me, so I

just carried on with what I was doing as she prepared her own breakfast. I stayed in the kitchen, and had a standing breakfast, while she went into the living-room.

We had already discussed, the day before, what time I would need to leave, and it had been she who had suggested the ten o'clock bus, so there was no conversation at all as I finished my breakfast, washed and dried my dishes, and went back upstairs to get what meagre stuff I had with me, ready to leave.

Leaning on the window sill, looking out through the window, and seeing nothing at all beyond the jumbled thoughts in my head, I waited until it was time to go.

Pauline actually called, eventually, the first time she had spoken anything.

'It's time we left for the bus. Are you ready?'

'Yes, OK I'm coming down.'

We left by the back door. Pauline turned to lock the door and we set off, together, on the short walk to the bus-stop, covering the same ground, in reverse, that we had gone over when I had first arrived.

I was aware of every step of it, painfully remembering the coldness of my arrival, and remembering the foreboding that I had had at that time, which seemed a lifetime away. She walked a little ahead of me. Not a word was spoken.

We arrived at the stop. Everything was very quiet. Even though there was a small Tesco store, open, right opposite the bus-stop, there wasn't a soul around. Pauline looked at the printed timetable on the bus-stance, to check that she had been correct about the time of the bus, then stepped back saying nothing and looking up the road in the direction from which the bus would come.

I said to her, 'I think I'm capable of catching a bus on my own. There isn't any point in you hanging around.'

'Alright,' she replied,' sotto voce, and she just turned away from me and walked off. I had to think back fifty seven years, almost, and London, to remember when I had been as lonely as I was at that moment.

The bus didn't come. I stood waiting and looking up the road to see if there was any sign of it, stepping out onto the road to look, as if that would compel it to come, but at twenty past ten, it was obvious that there wasn't going to be a bus. I was panicking a little, because I didn't have a huge amount of time to get into Chelmsford, and to transfer to the airport bus. There was no choice, I had to phone Pauline, and ask her if she could get me a taxi.

'Pauline, I'm sorry. The bus hasn't turned up. Do you have the number for a taxi?'

'That often happens here on a Sunday. The buses here just seem to run as they please. I'll call a taxi. You'd better come back to the house. The taxi will find my place easier than where you are. I'll ring you back if there is a problem.'

I didn't know whether she was wanting me to go back to the house so that she could see me again. I very much doubted it. I wasn't going to risk it. I didn't want to see her again, anyway.

'Thank you. I'll just wait outside your gate,' I replied. The last time I was to speak to her for several months, but at the time, I thought it would be the last time ever.

Sitting on the low wall by the car parking area, just

outside Pauline's back gate, I deliberately avoided looking at the house.

The taxi arrived within a few minutes. I got into the front passenger seat and I told the driver where I was going, and that I was catching the airport bus. As the taxi pulled away, I was compelled to take one last look back at the house. I saw Pauline at the window of the bedroom that I had stayed in, standing just where I had stood on those miserable occasions when I had been trying so hard to make some sense of what had happened. As she watched the taxi draw away, Pauline lifted her hand, and she waved. In that split second, I swear that she metamorphosed into Pauline Phizacklea, aged seventeen, waving me off from Leicester all those years ago. I didn't wave back, and I turned back to face the front. It was a fleeting epiphany, and then it was gone, and so was I.

'We'll have to be a bit quick, then,' the taxi driver said. 'Are you going away somewhere nice?' he then asked.

'I'm going home……I've just been here for a few days to visit a fr…to visit someone I know.'

'Right. Where's home then?'

'I live in Scotland.'

'Right. You won't be so warm up there then,' he laughed.

I think I would have had to stand at the Arctic Circle naked, to be as cold as I've been this last three days, I thought.

'No.' That was all the conversation we had before we got to Chelmsford. He saw that I was not in a talkative mood.

'There's your bus pal. You made it OK…Thanks,' he said as I gave him the fare, and a tip, in Scottish notes. It bothered him not at all. 'Have a good flight.'

I think I had become an automaton by then, just carrying out all necessary moves mechanically, as I boarded the airport bus, and paid for my ticket, with coins this time.

*

Some images from our past are so strong that they can be recalled, vividly, for the rest of our lives. Why this is the case may seem obvious, sometimes, but on other occasions, the reason for such strong retention is not clear at all. Some of my memories of my time with Pauline are as fresh now, as they were in the 1950's, yet others have vanished completely. Pauline could remember every detail of some of those things that I have forgotten, whilst having no recall, at all, of some of my strongest memories. Time and imagination edits, and embellishes things, I'm sure, but recall can be very powerful.

When I was young, probably around five or six years old, my mother took me to see Santa Claus, and this incident flashes into my mind every year when I walk down any High Street, past the department stores with Santas in them. My excitement was built up over weeks before the event, and I got more and more excited as the time approached to go and see him.

As I stood in the queue awaiting my turn, holding my mother's hand, and hoping that I could hold the wee in before I got to the great man, I observed him with the children before me as each, in turn, sat on his lap, and told him, in a huge variety of different voices, what they wanted for Christmas. I looked him over, because I don't think I had seen him before. He was, of course, an old man, with a scrawny face, and white hair that was askew on his head, and with a scruffy, garden gnome type of hat on, held in place with kirby-grips. His white beard, with non-matching texture to his hair was clearly hooked over his ears with wires, which was making it difficult for him to keep his horn-rimmed glasses on straight. The beard clearly had an independent existence of its own, and Santa was constantly pushing it back in place, to match the hole in it with his mouth. His red cloak was a double-breasted affair, held closed with a red, tied on belt, and it was trimmed with, what looked like, cotton-wool. It had become a bit detached, in places, at some time, and had been fixed back in place with large blanket stitches. Below that he had on brown corduroy trousers, and rather muddy wellie boots. The most fascinating thing about him was his denture juggling. His teeth were constantly clicking around in his mouth, sometimes protruding beyond his lips, as he spoke to the children. It came to my turn.

'So, what would you like Santa to bring you then me duck?' he asked, 'clickety clack.' (Santa, clearly, came from Leicester.)

'I'd like a blackboard and easel, please,' I replied, wriggling on his knee, because I really did need a wee then. I had no idea what a blackboard and easel was, but I knew for sure that I wanted one, because my mother had been telling me so for weeks. And I loved the word 'easel.'

'That's nice, me duck. I think I could manage that for you.'

'Thank you, Santa,' I squeaked, as I jumped down from his knee.

I ran to my mother and took her hand, as she smiled down at me, and asked,

'Well. Was that nice? What did you ask him for?'

(My sister figures absolutely nowhere in this recall, at all, even though, I presume, she must have been there somewhere).

The thing is, that in spite of all the evidence to the contrary; despite everything I had seen about Santa Claus, I left there convinced that I had just sat on the lap of the 'magic' man who was going to come down my chimney, with a blackboard and easel. Because my imagination had been so fired up, for weeks, in preparation for that moment, I was willing to ignore, completely, what I had seen, and what my brain was so clearly telling me; dismiss it entirely, because what I wanted to believe was much stronger in my mind than what I had seen.

As hollow, and as empty as I felt on that flight to Edinburgh, I knew that I wanted to ignore every scrap of what I had experienced over that last few days; to cast off the hurt she had inflicted upon me, and believe the fantasy that I had gone down there with. I knew that it wasn't over, even if I did have to work very hard at convincing myself.

On the aircraft home I had become very calm; in a state of suspended animation, I think. What had happened to me was not in my thoughts. I was just thinking about picking up the car at the airport; hoping I had change for the parking machine; 'no, I don't need that, do I, it takes cards;' had to get into some weeding in that garden when I get home, and the grass will probably need mowing, for sure.

Driving, mechanically, back home from Edinburgh to North East Fife, I saw nothing, heard nothing, smelt nothing.

On arriving home, life took over. There were practical, routine things to get on with. Food was needed, so I had to go into Cupar, to Tescos. At home I got on with all of those domestic chores, that take up the greater part of our lives. I did not, consciously, shut anything out at all, things just shut themselves out, and the sun was shining. That 'child's' protection from the 'bogie man,' I have found, on many occasions, never really leaves us, and will slip back in, reflexively, when we need it to look after us.

No-one had been told that I was going down to Chelmsford to see Pauline. In fact, no-one knew about Pauline, except Gordon and Lili, so it was no great problem.

This was Sunday, June 24th, and Gordon always phoned me on a Sunday, especially since his mother died, because he was concerned that I would be lonely. There were times, I knew, that he felt guilty for being so far away, and unable to come and see me. I tried to get through to him that I wasn't lonely, and that I was fine.

That afternoon, I was fine. There was no pain; no trauma, and I thought nothing about the previous three days, at all, as I just pottered about, doing things. I did think about it later, though, because I decided to tell Gordon some of what had happened.

The phone-call from Gordon came at about a quarter past eleven, as of his usual time of calling, when I was relaxing, with my feet up, with a whisky and a book.

'Hi, dad… OK?' came his regular greeting.

'Hi… Sure, I'm fine. You?'

'Yes, great. It was the 'British Judo Masters,' in Wales, yesterday, and I took silver.'

'Right. Very good…… I flew down to see Pauline, in Chelmsford, for a few days. I just got back this afternoon.' I said. I should have enquired more about the judo, I know, but I needed to get this off my chest. Even so, talking about it was having no affect on me; no throat lumps, or hesitations.

'And?' he asked, with a bit of surprise in his voice.

'And, nothing, I'm afraid, Gordon… She is a very old lady, Gordon, with all sorts of medical problems. I didn't recognise her at all. We had not the slightest thing in common; and she's got a cat! ' That was about all I was going to tell him, for now, anyway.

'I'm sorry, dad.' There was a genuine note of sadness in his voice. 'I didn't want to say anything before, but I'm not surprised. I knew that, if it was the case, you would find out for yourself, soon enough. You've got to remember, dad, that people of your age are much older than you. You need a woman in her forties, not her seventies. You're still very active. Most folk of your age are halfway to the grave.'

'Thanks, loving son, that's very kind of you, but if you

don't mind, I think I'll pass. Women are more trouble than they're worth… I'll stick to whisky, and gardening.'

The following week brought a lot of nice weather, and I got out on the bike a lot, touring around a few of the Highland glens in Perthshire and Stirlingshire, and it released a lot of tension, that had probably still been there, and the feeling of freedom was really good.

'It was about the time I went see friends…about Thursday or Friday I think? And it was then that I told them all about Pauline. It was also when they told me that they thought I would have wanted to wait awhile. It was when I told them about her medical problems that sounded alarm bells. I didn't tell them anything more, then, than I had told Gordon. I think I just felt humiliated by the whole experience. No, that's not true, I felt stunned, and deflated, and I think that if I'd said anymore, it could have set me off again, where I had been.'

On the Saturday, July 1st, I got a call from Martin and Mandy, who were on their way back to Spain the following day, and we had a long chat. It was then that they suggested I should think about going to live out there. It was something I hadn't thought about before, but right at that moment, it was suddenly starting to sound very attractive. They said I could go out there the following week, to stay with them, and I could talk it over with Jack, a friend of theirs, who was close to everything that went on out in Empuria. I knew the area well, having been there many times, and I always liked it there.

'You could just come out short term, for the winter, to start with, just to see how you like it then, because you haven't been here in the winter, have you?'

'No, I haven't. That sounds like a brilliant idea. I could just use some winter sun, after the two winters we have just had. Any idea when you would be willing to put up with me?'

'OK, let's see; this is Sunday. We'll need a few days to get things tidied out a bit, and some food in. How about Friday 6th?'

'No problem, as far as I can see at the moment. I should get an 'Easyjet' from here, and a 'Ryanair' from London to Girona. Is that alright? Just one last thing. How long do you want me there for?'

'Does a week suit you? If that's alright with you just ring us back when you've booked your flights, so that we will know what time to pick you up at the airport.'

That all sounded really good, and I was beginning to get wound up already. Living in Spain! Brilliant! Why had I never thought of it? What a solution. I knew that I would need to get rid of the cottage in Fife, soon, anyway. There was too much garden, and too much maintainence involved with old cottages, and one day it would be beyond me. I needed to be near a bus-route, too, not five miles away from one, as I was in Baldinnie. What would happen, if for some reason I wasn't able to drive?

CHAPTER 12

Being old has plenty of baggage; as my old mother-in-law used to say, 'auld age disnae come itsel', but, we do learn things during a long life, and one particular lesson stood out for me, at this time; our bodies and our minds are very capable of colluding together to lie to us. They probably do it far more often than we think, because it is done in such a sneaky manner, that we do not notice it happening. It is , undoubtedly, the mind that is in charge of the process, and my mind had said to my body, 'OK, this guy's taken quite a pounding, so let's you and I get things settled down a bit, and give him some time to recover. You won't have to do much, because you didn't get the punishment. It was all me that took the beating, so all you have to do is go along with what I tell you, and everything will be alright.'

So, just one week after the 'Hell trip,' to Pauline's,

getting excited and all wound up about the prospect of going to live in Spain, I was on my way out there to spend an exploratory week with Martin and Mandy. Body and mind relaxed, and feeling good.

I rode down to Coventry on the bike on July 5th, to spend the night with Margaret and Terry, my sister-in-law, and her husband. The following day, on leaving the bike at their house, Terry took me to Birmingham Airport, and I flew to Girona, where Martin and Mandy picked me up, for the drive to Empuriabrava. This region of the Costa Brava used to be very busy with British holiday makers, at the time when foreign trips abroad were at the beginning of the trend, back in the 50's and 60's, but had become much quieter since the popular areas had opened up further south. It was around twenty kilometres, or so, from the French border, on the Mediterranean, with the beautiful Pyrenees as a backdrop.

Martin and Mandy's house is close to both the town and the beach, and I was looking forward to a relaxing break, very much, and also looking forward to doing some forward planning, with a life in the sun, on my own, very high in my thoughts. I felt any cares that remained melt away, quickly, and it was no problem for me to relate to my friends.

I told them of my adventure with Pauline. I told them more than I had told other people, actually, because I related the whole story about our past; about the internet search for Pauline, and about the, abortive, visit to Chelmsford. They were kept in the dark, however, about the trauma that I had suffered. I don't know whether I was feeling the shame of what had happened, or whether I was just afraid of reviving the pain.

It was lovely to just sit and talk, over a drink, out in the sun. Martin and Mandy showed mixed feelings about what I told them. They were intrigued by the story; pleased that I was moving on after the loss of Rosemary, (they had known Rosemary well, because it was out there we had all met, many years earlier, and we had shared a lot of holidays with them), but they were a bit disappointed that things had not worked out. Martin and Mandy, like most of my friends, wanted to see me happy. Everyone knew the years of caring for Rosemary had taken its toll on me, and felt that I was due a break.

The week was spent very lazily, for me anyway, because I wasn't doing the driving around the many villages we visited, and places we ate in. Every morning, before Martin and Mandy were up, I went to the beach for a swim, then back to the house for breakfast, out on the terrace in the morning sun. The life-style was seriously growing on me, and arrangements were being put in place to find me somewhere to live out there, for a trial eight months over the winter.

About halfway through the week there, I took a walk along to the 'Montserrat,' (the supermarket), to get a thank-you gift for my hosts, for their kindness to me. Only during my week there had it become evident to me just how much I had needed that therapy, and how much recovering I had needed to do.

My brain and body were still looking after me very nicely, but I was about to do something very unpredictable.

I had learned, very early in my counselling training, the remarkable fact that we have very little control over what we do, because our conscious behaviour constitutes only about four or five percent of our being. We are flying on auto-pilot for around ninety five percent of our lives, and that is not including sleeping time. It's simple to understand, really, that if we had to make a conscious decision before every action, we would never get out of bed in the morning, so, naturally, we spend most of our existence in the subconscious, and just come out of there when decisions have to be made. We may be aware of the decision, at the time, but we are rarely aware of why we made it. I was about to do something without the slightest idea why, and it was an act that was to completely change my future, and send all my marvellous plans into oblivion.

As I was about to leave the supermarket, I bought a postcard. I wrote on it; addressed it, and posted it.

There was no logical reason, whatsoever, why I should want to contact Pauline, in fact, quite the opposite. Having pretty much recovered from my bruising encounter, why on earth would I want a return bout? Was it just spur of the moment, when I saw the postcard rack? Had it been in my mind when I left the house? I have read the postcard several times, since, and I am still completely in the dark about it. I even took the blame for what had happened during the 'horror' three days! I claimed that it had been my over-emotional state that had brought it about! I still can't believe it, and what I find most difficult of all to believe, is that I signed it, 'Tony.' Thank God I didn't put kisses on it. There was something in my subconscious at work, certainly.

The card was a picture of a solitary tree, on a rocky Spanish shore. Was that, somehow, subconsciously symbolic? Had I sent it, expecting a response? No matter how much I try to analyse it, there is no answer to be found, and so what? What's the point in trying to find answers? Nothing will be changed, even if it was possible to find reasons for doing it.

The card, it turned out, was exactly what Pauline had hoped for. Not 'the card', exactly, but a straw to clutch at. Something to give her the chance to open up a dialogue. Although she confessed later that she had determined to contact me, at some point, and on some pretext, to see if she could rekindle the relationship, and repair the damage, so the card had taken that dilemma out of her hands, and delivered me, 'trussed' and 'oven ready', into her hands.

Flying into Birmingham, on my return from Spain, I was met at the airport by Terry. I stayed with Margaret and Terry for a few days in Coventry. It was always pleasant, and relaxing to stay with them, because I am an 'active relaxer', and they could normally find me a job or two to do.

After five days with Margaret and Terry, I got on the bike, and rode up to Norfolk, to spend three days with my sister, Elizabeth. I didn't tell her anything about my dealings with Pauline, and then I was homebound.

It had been twelve days since I had sent the postcard to Pauline, from Spain, and as I only had a 'desktop' at that time, I hadn't been able to check my emails since I'd left Scotland, on July 6th. Among the pile in my inbox there was an email from Pauline, headed, 'Friends?'

'Thanks for the postcard. I had a feeling that I had offended you so much that you were going to ride off into the sunset again. I didn't mean to hurt you. That said, I think it is much better for us to remain friends, than to complicate things, so I would like to hear from you now and again.' There followed some usual Pauline chatty stuff, about the weather and the garden, and she ended the mail, 'Bye for now, Pauline ' and she even gave it one 'kiss.'

Pauline's emails always had that air of daily life about them, fixing me firmly in the realms of 'normal' life. I had the feeling that if there had been a major catastrophe, somewhere close, she would not be able to comment on it without also mentioning how the flowers were growing in the garden.

The email was dated July 17th, exactly one week after I had posted the postcard to her in Spain, and her email had been in my inbox for six days before I read it. I had a sneaky feeling of pleasure, knowing that Pauline would have been wondering why I hadn't replied.

I had very mixed feelings. I know I was pleased to receive the email, but it irritated the wound a little. An instant return to any kind of 'good old friends' situation, or a re-establishment of the fondness we had enjoyed, before I had visited her in Chelmsford, was not on my radar. I know that I didn't trust her not to hurt me again, and she had said things that had gone far too deeply into my fragile state to just be dismissed, and forgotten. I remember telling her, later, that it had been more like an amputation than a wound, and it was something I would just have to learn to live with, because it couldn't be 'unamputated.' Contact, 'now and again', seemed alright by me. More 'again' than 'now,' the more appropriate option. Apart from anything else, my impending move to Spain had priority in my mind, at that time.

Pauline had sent her email on July 17th, and I didn't get to read it until July 23rd. I sent a very terse reply on August 2nd. – 'That's me back online. Contact you soon. Glenn.' I returned the compliment of just one 'kiss.'

Pauline phoned me on Sunday, August 5th, and we spoke, cordially, for about half an hour, and said very little. The air was tense, but I knew that she was, genuinely, trying to be pleasant. The conversation was mostly about our respective families; the gardens; the weather, and just about anything trivial, and pointlessly non-commital.

I decided, however, to introduce her to my intention to go and live in Spain, although I just said that I was in the process of an 'exciting project,' that I would tell her more about later. I think my intention was probably to give her something intriguing to think about, and to get her worried. I also told her that I made rocking-horses. This, in itself, is pathetically trivial, I know, but it was the motive behind it, I think, that makes it significant. I was trying to be impressive. I was undoubtedly boasting about my artistic talent, and I said that I would send her a photograph of a rocking-horse that I still had, and which I used for a demonstration model. I posted it on August 6th, and received an email reply on the 7th.

'Loved the rocking horses. I'm impressed.' Well, that had been what was intended, so I was very pleased to see that I had hit the target with that one. 'What is this exciting news you are going to tell me?' My intention had been to create a mystery, and to keep her in suspense, so I was, smugly, content that the desired effect seemed to have been achieved there, also. I'm not sure if I was being consciously devious at that point, but it was clearly obvious to me later. There is no doubt in my mind now that I had begun to evolve a clear sense of direction. I was getting in control of the situation, and becoming manipulative.

Whether or not either of us ever intended to stick to the idea of contact just 'now and then,' as at first agreed, I don't know, but it didn't happen. Regular emails, and Sunday phone calls, quickly became the established routine, with nothing much being said by either of us. However, it was what wasn't being said, and what was deliberately being ignored, that was the most obvious message ringing loudly in the background. The June trauma was never mentioned, but was always present in every conversation we had. Our emails remained wholly uncommitted, and signed off with no shows of affection, that is up until I told her, on Saturday, August 18th, that I was going to live in Spain.

Since my visit to Spain, in July, all I had been waiting for was word from my friends, Martin and Mandy, that somewhere had been found for me to live for the trial eight months that I intended spending there over the winter. I received word from them on August 14th, that accommodation had been found, and all that was left to do was to provide dates, and agree on a rental. Over the next few days it was decided that I would cross to France on the ferry on Sunday, September 30th, to take up residence on Monday, October 1st. It was my intention to return to Scotland at the end of May, 2013.

Going to live in Spain was still very much in my mind, and I firmly believed, at that time, that it was pretty much a done deal; not just for the winter, but permanently, and after what had happened back in June, Pauline didn't really figure in my plans. I was pleased that we were in contact again, and I was pleased that we were getting closer, even though neither of us would have admitted that at the time, but I saw my future place in the sun; on my own.

On Tuesday, August 14th I sent Pauline an email to tell her that I was ready to reveal my exciting news. I told her that I would let her know everything, on the phone on Saturday, August 18th. It had to be Saturday because I would be away on the Sunday. I was going up to Lossiemouth to do some work for my disabled brother-in-law. Pauline was obviously worried about what I was going to tell her. I know that I had been deliberately building the tension; it was a 'control' thing. On August 15th I had received a terse email from her.

'Am I going to like this revelation or not?'

Pauline hadn't even signed it.

'Love it, or be totally indifferent to it. No pain attached, so don't be afraid.' I replied. On Saturday, August 18th I phoned her, as promised, and told her about my plans. The news was met with silence, then…

'I'm surprised. I wasn't expecting that.' The flatness in her voice was very striking, and it pleased me. I wanted her to feel rejected. I know it was cruel, but I was feeling cruel. I told her, with relish, that I was looking forward to going, very much, and told her that I intended lapping up the sun, and the freedom.

'I'll still keep in touch, if that's what you want,' I told her, 'and who knows, you might get out to visit me sometime.' I don't look back on what I did with any kind of pleasure, because I know that I was deliberately sounding out her feelings. The phone call did not last long, and I knew that I had upset her. I intended, tenaciously, pursuing that course until I was able to judge, with more certainty, what her feelings were.

What my mind was playing at, I don't know, because I had no intention, as far as I was aware, of resuming any kind of romantic attachment. I still didn't have a lap-top then, so when I went to Lossiemouth I completely ignored Pauline until I returned home.

I arrived home on August 26th and I still continued to hold back on contacting her. I had not told her what day I would be home, before I went. On August 29th I received, what I would call a very significant email. If I were to make a judgement, I would say that that email marked another defining moment in the development of our future. There was a slight sense of panic in the opening of her communication.

'I haven't heard from you for ages. What have you been up to?' She then told me of an article that she had read in a Saturday newspaper that had brought back 'so many fond memories.' She said she would send it to me. The most significant feature of the email, however, was the ending – she signed herself off, 'Love, Pauline.' Not only 'Love,' but also two 'kisses.' That was the first show of affection shown between us since the resumption of communications. It may seem slight, but its intent was clear to me, I think!

I replied later in the day, explaining that I had been very busy at Lossiemouth, and I told her that I would phone her on Sunday, 2nd September. To indicate that I had noticed her shift in sentiment, I signed off my email, 'Love, Glenn,' but, so as not to seem too eager, I gave it just one 'kiss.'

When I received the newspaper article that Pauline had mentioned, I was not only amazed by the remarkable number of coincidences in it, that matched our young experiences, but I read beyond the article to something that, I thought, Pauline was trying to tell me. The writer, (Colin Dunne, Daily Mail, Saturday, August 25th 2012), had said that, prior to the 'swinging sixties' he and his girlfriend, Pauline, had invented sex, in 1954. Not only was she 'Pauline', but she had 'green eyes;' she was 'sixteen;' she was a 'farmer's daughter,' and she lived 'about two miles out of town.' The best I can do is to let you read my reply, and you will get the significance, not only of the amazing coincidences contained within the article, but also the importance of the tone of my reply.

'I really enjoyed the article. It was very funny, and, as you said, it brought back so many memories. I was amazed at the familiar bits – Pauline, aged sixteen; 1954; green eyes, farmer's daughter; two miles outside of town. She even rode a bike, and to top it all, there was a river-bank scene.'

The writer's moment of passion had been in a cowshed, so I wrote,

'I have to say that I am happy to have our river-bank as our iconic moment, complete with peeping-tom, in place of their cowshed moment.'

The writer also described sexual discovery as being 'like exploring Africa,' and he also said that their sex education at school had been awkward stuff about frogspawn and tadpoles. Women's breasts he described as being like 'icecream cones.'

I wrote, 'It may have been because I was away such a lot of the time that our 'African exploration' was more rapid than theirs. I certainly remember that I had my hand on the left 'icecream cone' at about the time that Errol Flynn was leading his fateful five hundred into 'The valley of death.' 'Another thing I remember is that tights hadn't been invented, and there was nothing more sensual than stocking-tops and suspenders. The first time my hand strayed above your stocking-top into no-man's-land I swear I heard Angels singing.'

In the article the other Pauline had tears in her eyes, because she thought that she could never be as happy again. I said that,

'I hope you will be able to be as happy again, some day. In fact, if our river-bank passion hadn't been interrupted we would have had 'tadpoles' to worry about. History really would have been changed. I don't think we 'called it love,' it was love. The fact that you kept that flame burning for so many years before you stopped loving me, is, I think, testament to that. For my part, although I did not keep the love alive, the memories never died, and the fact that I felt an overwhelming need to be in contact with you again, must say something. I too am an incurable romantic and I am very happy that we are communicating again. Are you happy?'

I ended my email, 'Love, Glenn,' and I gave it two kisses. Clearly, commitment was beginning.

That was September 10th, and that the tone had changed, was indisputable. Her return email cemented the change;

'Yes, I am very happy. I loved the email you sent. It's been a lovely warm day, today.'

Both of us were fully aware of the cat and mouse mind games that we had been playing since July, and, in truth, I think we were enjoying them. Neither of us knew, however, just where we were going, but I do think that we were both hoping for the outcome that we arrived at. The June meeting had been a hammer-blow, to both of us, because Pauline did admit that the worst thing she had had to face was the realisation that her own pain was self-inflicted. The immense feeling of relief we both shared, as that trauma slipped away from us, gave us the strength to go forward.

Phone-calls and many emails saw us get closer by the hour, and just nine days after that newspaper article email, on September 19th, it had reached the stage when I was beginning to regret that I was going to live in Spain. My email of September 19th confirmed that.

'My departure is getting very close now, and a new adventure that I would have relished a few years ago seems daunting now. I think that the years of virtual house-arrest have taken their toll on my confidence. I know that when

I get out there I'll be fine, but at the moment I feel that I am putting miles between us, just when we are coming together. It's nonsense, really, because we are just as far apart when I'm here, maybe even further, since you have said that you will come out to Spain.'

That email from me was probably the beginning of the acceptance, by both of us, that we had reached the point that it had been obvious we had been heading for, and by the end of the month we had committed to each other, and it was arranged that I would fly back from Spain on October 14th, when we would spend two weeks together, and visit all the members of our two families for introductions. We decided to break the news by phone to them all before then. That would be the first time that we had seen each other since the disastrous end of June.

I was thinking about that. Thinking very hard about it.

Because it had been three months since the pain of June, it seemed as if the communications leading up to our really coming together had gone on for a long time, but in reality, it had happened in just a few weeks.

At the beginning of our reconnection we had been small people in the centre of a wide angle view, with a lot of things in the same frame, all impinging on our lives, but by the end of September the lense had slowly drawn us to the centre of attention, and we had become the whole of the picture. The background had slipped out of the frame, and we had pushed everything else out of our lives. But, all of a sudden, the lense panned out again to the wide angle, and the rest of the world joined us, and I was back in a bewildering panorama of uncertainty, and I became afraid.

On September 23rd Margaret and Terry, came to spend a week with me. The plan was that I would drive them home to Coventry, on Saturday, September 29th, stay the night with them before crossing to France on a Sunday ferry, and then the drive to Spain.

That plan had to be abandoned when my car broke down, with a serious fault, on Friday, September 28th. It was then decided that Margaret and Terry would fly home, and that I would then go down to Coventry on the motor-bike the following day; leave the bike at their house, and fly to Spain from Birmingham on Wednesday, October 3rd, so that I could get the keys to the house I would be living in.

The omens were not good, right from the start, when the car broke down, and the more superstitious may well have shut themselves in a darkened room for a couple of days, at that stage, but I persevered. The ride down to Coventry was hideous, through a howling gale, reducing the speed limit on the M6 to 40 mph, and with horizontal rain lashing into my face.

No-one had been told anything about Pauline, except Gordon, and I hadn't told him that Pauline and I were about to come together again, but I decided to tell Margaret and Terry, before I flew to Spain, because when I flew back I would be going stay with Pauline for a week. I felt that they should know of our plans first, because it would be their house I would be returning to on October 12th, before joining Pauline on the 14th.

They were not at all happy about what I told them, and I left for Spain, on October 3rd, under a very heavy cloud.

It was good to relax in Spain. I was living in an apartment quite close to the beach, with a balcony overlooking a marina. The sun was warm, and the place was quiet, as the tourist season was over. I determined to get the stress off my back, and to spend the nine days before I went back, to be with Pauline, putting myself in the right frame of mind.

Our last time together had come back to me in a big way, and I was even losing sleep over it. Over and over again I tried to imagine the scenario of our coming together again, and over and over again I started trembling, and I was consumed with trepidation. I knew that if I went to her in that same mind-set, it would be disastrous. I am sure that everyone has done as I was doing, and rehearsed some impending meeting; trying hard to think through every eventuality, but I kept seeing her sneering at me, and belittling me. We hadn't mentioned it over the weeks we had been coming together, and I had no idea whether or not she felt the same tension. It must have been in her mind; after all, it was not something trivial. We had spoken of being in bed together, and I let my mind experience those pleasures, but even that filled me with worry.

Not having my car out with me was a big handicap, and the bad news was that it would probably be some weeks before I got it back. I decided, therefore, that I would take the bike back to Spain, when I returned on October 26th, after being with Pauline.

Arriving at Pauline's house on the 14th, encased in bike leathers, I felt the tension leave me, as I took her into my arms, awkwardly, and she laughed at me; not aggressively, but fondly, because it was bizarre. My leathers were cold, and as unyielding as a suit of armour.

Her demeanour was instantly reassuring; friendly, and loving, and I did not see that woman who had been there in June. Even Maisie, the cat, smiled at me, and rubbed herself against my boot, purring. What an enormous difference a loving, warmly smiling face made to Pauline's appearance, and to Maisie's. I held Pauline to me for a long time, unable to speak.

After I had changed, and eaten, we sat, entwined, on the settee for hours into the evening, watching things move silently across the television screen. Very little was said, and very little needed saying. Pauline still hadn't said that she loved me, and as far as words were concerned I would still have to 'wait and see,' but the words weren't necessary now. I had no doubt that I loved her, and no doubt that she loved me. But, the night was still to come, and we would be in bed together for the first time for well over half a century. I remembered well her 17 year old body, and the ecstacy of making love to her. She was still very beautiful, and that spiteful old woman from June had disappeared, and I desperately wanted her, but I was scared; not about her, but about me.

When the time came for bed, I was pleased that Pauline took the initiative. I could sense that she was nervous, but she told me to go upstairs and get into bed, and she would follow me up after a few minutes.

I was trembling, as I prepared to get into bed. I had anticipated this moment for weeks, never quite knowing what it would be like, and letting my imagination make of it what it could. I was scared; my mouth was dry, and I licked my lips as I climbed into bed.

As if she sensed that I was now in bed, I heard Pauline climb the stairs. She came into the bedroom, briefly, and left again to go into the bathroom.

Coming back into the bedroom again, she started doing things that were obviously designed to use up time, delaying the moment when she had to get into the bed.

Sensing her shyness, I closed my eyes, and pointedly turned my head on the pillow, to show that I wasn't watching her undress. I heard the rustle of her clothes as she removed them, and I caught a quick glimpse of her black satin underwear, as she climbed into her side of the bed.

I could feel her body trembling, as I am sure she could feel mine. I turned to her, and took her into my arms, and touched her temple with my finger-tips, and smiled. She smiled back, and she kissed me.

It was a moment that I could never have believed would happen. I moved to her and pulled her to me… and as a lover I was a complete failure.

There was an implosion of 'June' inside my head. The humiliation of that time flooded my brain; 'It was just kiddie love,' was in my head. 'You were nothing special, and well down the league-table,' hit me with blow after blow. It was as if I was competing with her previous conquests, and I crumpled, literally, as well as mentally. I was an utter failure. The tears came and Pauline tried to help me, but I couldn't be helped. She said,

'Don't worry, it will be alright tomorrow. You are just

nervous.' She made suggestions as to how we may improve the experience, and all I could think was, 'God, she's going to try and teach me how to make love.' I don't know how I was behaving. I desperately needed her tenderness, and I tried to cuddle her. She said,

'I am tired, and we should sleep. That's your side of the bed, and this is mine, so let's get that straight right now, and get some sleep.'

I felt miserably wretched, and rejected. I was inadequate, but not in a failed manhood way, but in a failed human being kind of way. I was desperately lonely; humiliated and useless. Sleep was out of the question, although I tried, and failed in that too. I needed her so much at that moment, and she had pushed me away. I lay, staring at the ceiling, afraid. I was scared to go to sleep in case I touched her in the night, and her rebuke had seemed so stern; even threatening. I thought that 'June' had returned.

When I was sure that she was asleep, I crept out of bed and went to the bathroom. I have no idea what time it was, I didn't check. It wasn't important. I sat on a bathroom stool for a long time, going over the horrors of the experience, and trying to examine my options.

As far as I was concerned, the future had disappeared, and there could be no 'us.' The more I thought about it, the more I felt that I should leave. I was intent on quietly creeping back into the bedroom; packing my bags, and leaving. I was sure that Pauline had felt let down, and I thought she was angry and disappointed with me, and would be quite happy for me to leave.

I crept back into the bedroom. Daylight was beginning to filter through the light summer curtains, and I could see Pauline's face on her pillow. Being warm, she had pushed the duvet down from her upper body, and I could not keep back the tears as I looked at her, sleeping so peacefully, and she was seventeen again.

Within my head there was a dual dilemma – my inability; my impotence, and her rejection of me when I needed her the most. The first, I felt better able to deal with, because, even though I knew it was down to what had happened in June, I believed that it was something within my power to put right. Her rejection was more difficult, because it came from her, and it was out of my hands. It hit me the hardest because it seemed so cruel, and it frightened me, because it brought back the 'June Pauline' for the first time since we had come back together. I sat on my side of the bed, and tried to think of this situation from her point of view.

My bed had been empty for only a short time, but Pauline had been on her own for over thirty years. She had said, 'I will have forgotten so much. You will have to teach me.' I had taken that as ironic at the time, but what if she really meant it? The whole experience must be very frightening to her. Her bed has been hers, and hers alone for so long that she must learn to share it again with someone else. I had been trying to see into her head, from my point of view, and had probably got it completely wrong. With my usual selfishness, I was asking the questions, and giving the answers, without having the slightest idea how Pauline felt. I must give it a chance, and try to be understanding.

I climbed, quietly, back into the bed, and tried not to disturb her. I moved towards her, and snuggled into her back. She gave a slight murmur, and moved her body into me. The light of the breaking dawn was getting brighter, showing through the curtains as I closed my eyes.

CHAPTER 13

I t is always easier, long after an event, to see it clearer in hindsight. That may be because we are able to devote more time to our deliberations, or it may be because, not being with it any more, we just rationalise it, and come to wholly erroneous conclusions. Whatever it was, when I thought about it, later, I felt that I should have seen it coming, because it had been rehearsed in my mind from the moment that Pauline had said that we would share her bed together.

Entering a situation in a state of nervousness is always fraught with danger, because the trepidations become self-fulfilling. I think I failed because I expected to fail. The worst of it was, that I blamed Pauline, because I felt that she had rejected me, but, the reality was, I had rejected myself.

In a way, it was almost a repeat of what had happened to us back in 1955. Pauline hadn't rejected me then. She was completely innocent, and had no idea what was going on inside my head. Even then I had rejected myself, because I lacked the confidence to believe in myself. When her mother wrote to me, it was not what she said that predicated my actions, it was me self-fulfilling. 'There, I told you so,' said my twisted mind, 'you're just not good enough.'

When Pauline awoke, she had no idea where my head had been in the night. Thank God she had the sense to recognise that there was something wrong with my thinking, which had to be put right. I don't know how I would have approached it, because I had been going over it in my shallow slumber for the short time that I slept. I am a coward in matters like that, and often shy away from doing what has to be done, because I am afraid of the consequences.

'We must talk, Glenn. We must talk now, because if we don't, we won't move on, and for our own sanity, it is imperative that I try and explain myself.'

'You do not have to explain yourself, Pauline, it is my problem, it was me who failed, and it is me who must put it right.'

'Not 'that' problem, I mean I must try and explain why I behaved like I did back in June, when I was so hideous to you.'

Pauline had arisen early after that painful first night, unaware of my machinations during the night, but very aware of the obvious dilemma that was between us. I was glad that it was she who raised the issue, because I had not been able to think of a way to do it.

Pauline was being very serious, but I knew she was right. Until that barrier, that stood between us, was broken down, we could only move forward, tentatively, pretending that there was nothing there.

'We do need to talk, pet. Yes we do, I know, but not only about the pounding you gave me in June, but also about me/us now, are you sure you feel like talking about it right now? It doesn't have to be now.' (That's it. Put it off. Even though I knew how imperative it was that we sorted out the problem, I was still shying away from it).

'It does need to be now, Glenn, it really does. I have given it all so much thought, and I have done my best to try and work out why I did it, but, to be honest, I don't think I really know. I can tell you how I felt, and, hopefully, we will be able to make something of it, between us. But, you are going to have to tell me things too.' She went on,

'that's the major problem between us. We came back together; you said you loved me, but I couldn't understand how you could say that when you had not long since told me you loved Rosemary. I knew I loved you, and when I left home, to meet you off the airport bus, I was so wanting to see you, and to be held by you. I loved you, Glenn, for always. I never stopped loving you, but you had had forty nine years of marriage with another woman, and it should have been me.'

'I know, Pauline; I knew how you must have hated me for what I did to you, all those years ago. I knew how much I had hurt you; how much pain I had caused you, and I could understand just how much it must have come back to you when you saw me. How could it be otherwise?

I was amazed that you hadn't shown that reaction right from the beginning. I did just 'swan' back into your life, but I didn't expect you to fall into my arms. I don't know what I expected; there is so much that goes on inside us, that we are just not aware of. I think I really expected you to tell me to get stuffed. I thought, often enough, that that was exactly what you would do, long before we actually spoke on the phone.'

'No, Glenn, you don't understand how I felt. When I told you that I had forgiven you, after I learned about my mother's letter, I meant it. That part of our lives was long gone, Glenn, and, you're right, you broke my heart, and I didn't think I could ever get over it. Unfortunately, I tried to get over it by marrying the first man who was kind to me, and who seemed so understanding in trying to help me get over you. Being 'unsullied' was a big deal then, and when I told John about you, he accepted that you and I had been lovers, and still agreed to marry me, and that went a long way to us getting married. I've told you this, already, Glenn, but none of that is the reason for why I behaved like I did in June.'

'Did you hate me, when you first saw me?'

'No, of course I didn't hate you, I've told you. I loved you, but as soon as I saw you on that bus stance, I was consumed with an overwhelming jealousy. I was jealous of Rosemary. I looked at you, and suddenly realised that you had been happily married for forty nine years, and I had been on my own, sometimes struggling to survive; to bring up two children; children that I had always wanted to be yours. You had a son; grandchildren and great grandchildren, and I had known about them; I had seen their photographs. Your mother used to tell me so much about them. At that time I didn't feel at all jealous. I was pleased that you were happily married, but as soon as I saw you get off that airport bus, it just flooded over me, and I had no control over what was happening inside me. For the whole three days I knew exactly what I was doing, and I couldn't stop myself doing it. I know you, Glenn, and even after fifty seven years, I know what hurts you. I watched your face. I knew every time I had scored a big hit, and I was compelled to move in and hit you harder. I even hated myself for what I was doing, but I just couldn't stop. I think I wanted to kill you. Not physically, of course, but I wanted to kill your spirit, and when I had you down on your knees, I had to slam you as hard as I possibly could.'

'You did a Hell of a good job. That final blow really was the 'coup de grace', and I couldn't rise from that.'

'I was up in your bedroom when you got in the taxi, but I don't think you saw me. I waved, like I used to, remember? But you didn't see me. As the taxi disappeared, I literally, screamed at myself, "you stupid, stupid bitch. What the Hell have you done?" and I threw myself on your bed and I howled, and howled for ages. I held your pillow in my arms, and I cursed myself, over and over again. I knew that I would never see you again. Your face said it all. You were so hurt.' The tears started to well in Pauline's eyes, as she relived the experience, and I felt my throat tighten as I recalled it too.

'I was actually bewildered, at that stage,' I said, 'there was no way I could make any sense of it. I thought it was all your defence mechanism working, when I did get around to trying to analyse it. You know me, that's what I do. I, in my arrogant stupidity, thought it was all about what I had done to you when you were seventeen…What about all the stuff you said? About me? About us? Was I really nothing to you? Did you really have a marvellous life?'

'You know damn well that you don't have to ask that. I was only seventeen, but I loved you beyond anything that ever was in my life. What you did hit me so hard, Glenn, that I really didn't want to go on living. After I had the children, I did have something to live for, but marvellous life? No, for most of it we were struggling to survive.'

'I'm sorry, Pauline, I really am. Nothing can change what happened, so saying sorry doesn't do anything at all, I know. I really have carried the guilt with me all of these years.'

'The time we had together then was the most wonderful time of my life, Glenn, I never forgot any of it, and nothing in my life ever came even close to it. I tried to rekindle it. I thought, after my divorce, that I would get married again, because I was still young, but it didn't happen. Once, I thought I was in love, but I wasn't. Anyway, he married someone else and phoned me to tell me that he wouldn't be seeing me again. I didn't cry, or get upset about it, I just got on with life. I had a lucky escape, really, he was a drunk.' Pauline laughed at that, but I thought of a time when she could have said the same about me.

'And the wonderful life that you had. All the boyfriends you ever wanted, whenever you wanted them?'

'Imagination. Imagination and lies, actually. I did have some relationships, I wasn't a nun, but nothing like I said in June. I did have a fairly lengthy relationship with one of the guys that I worked with at the bus company. It was never serious, and we never had any intentions to make it anything more than just enjoyment. I was having some fun, Glenn. My life was hardly a barrel of laughs, and I wanted to have some fun before I got too old. It became obvious that I would probably never remarry, and I wanted something of a life. It all happened in a very short space of time, anyway, because at the beginning of the seventies I went back to nursing. During my training I didn't date at all. I was too absorbed in my studies, and couldn't be bothered with men. I had two kids to bring up as well, so my time for anything else didn't exist. After I qualified, the only nursing post I could get was on permanent night-duty, and that lasted for three years. During that time I was always too exhausted and too tired to do anything. After that I went to the Nuffield in Brentwood, to work in the treatment room, and I was there until I retired. During that time I had one date, with a Norwegian bloke, that was a one-night-stand, and that was it. After that, dating didn't interest me. Anyway, how about you? I suppose you were the essence of purity, never a bed out of place?'

'No, I had a lot of relationships. After you, I vowed that I would never get married, and I meant it, but there were several women. Before I got married, that is. The first one after you got a really bad deal, actually, because she had to pay for what you'd done; well what I thought you'd done. There was one girl that I felt I could be serious with. After Suez, when I went back to Malta to work in Bighi hospital, in nineteen fifty seven. She was an art student, just out there for the summer with her parents, because her father worked alongside me in the dental department. It lasted only until she went back to England, and I think the only attraction had been that she was seventeen years old, and looked a bit like someone not too far away from me right now. I know I can be infuriatingly puritanical, and hypocritical, and I'll list every woman I ever bedded, if you want me to. If you've a couple of hours to spare.'

'Smartarse! No I don't want a list. How you spent your life is no concern of mine, and how I spent mine should be no concern of yours. You are with me, now, and that's all that matters to me, and that's all that should matter to you. What did you expect. That I should have sat around on the offchance that you might drop in some day? I did keep hopes alive, for years, but once your mother told me you were married, the bottom dropped out of my world. I knew then that that was it, and you were gone.'

'I love you Pauline, I love you dearly, and that we are together is all that matters. What you did in your life would have, genuinely, been of no concern of mine, but you used all of that as a weapon against me. You beat me in the face with all those men to destroy me, and put me up against them in some kind of league table. You did it on purpose, Pauline, you know you did, to hurt me as much as you could. That is what made them an issue. That is why I had to ask you about what you said. Once we have talked it through, hopefully, it will be an issue no more. You love me, and that makes me the luckiest man on earth, and when we have talked this through, I can kick all of those men out of our bed, and get on with loving you as I intend to. If I ever come even the tiniest bit close to hurting you, Pauline, please tell me. I want us, always, to be able to talk to each other. Misunderstandings destroyed us in the first place. We must never allow it to happen again.'

'I'm desperately sorry for what I did, Glenn, I really am, but there is no-one else in our bed but you and me. But, what about Rosemary?'

'What! What do you mean, what about Rosemary?'

'Rosemary, Glenn, I want to know about Rosemary. You married her instead of me, and I want to know about her. You told me how much you loved her. Is she still there?'

'Pauline, after what you felt about 'the letter,' are you sure about this?'

'Yes, I'm sure. I know it seems contradictory, but 'the letter' was a shock, because I wasn't expecting it at that time, but I'm past that now, and I really want to know everything. Did you really love her? Did you love her as much as you loved me? Was she anything like me? I hope we have exorcised your demons, Glenn, now you have to exorcise mine. I mean it. I still have stuff to get past as well, you know.'

That was something that had to be done. It was the first time that the 'June' debacle had been mentioned, and I was very pleased that it was Pauline who had raised it. Because of what happened the previous night, our first night together; the hangups I was suffering, because of what had happened in June, had to be resolved, or we could not have moved on. Everything she said about June was what I had believed had been the case, and more, but we had needed to talk about it. It couldn't remain in the head.

Telling her about Rosemary, I knew, would be more painful for her than it would be for me, and I did my best to be as sensitive about it as I could. Why-ever it is, I do not know, but it is always deflating to know that someone you love has loved someone else, in the past, even though it was a spouse. Perhaps it is just we old people who treasure that sense of exclusivity; that feeling that you can only, really, love one person, and any loves beyond that are second-hand. I saw those moments in Pauline's face when I needed to hold her hand, even to take her and kiss her during a pause. She listened quietly to what I told her, interrupting only occasionally, just to ask for some clarification. Because of Pauline's own health problems, it was natural that she would be closely interested to learn of the years that I had cared for Rosemary, especially during the five years of her dementia.

'Glenn, I know you love me, but you know that my lungs are bad. Do you really want to find yourself going through what could be more years of caring for an invalid, after all you had to do for Rosemary?'

'You exaggerated, didn't you, when you said that you only had about two years to live? Back in June, it was a part of your attack on me, wasn't it, to make me feel even worse than I already did?' The memory of her sneering it at me, back then, brought to mind the tears that I shed, and was ridiculed for.

'Yes, of course I was exaggerating, but my health is still not good, you know that. I am going to start a new course of treatment, soon, that should bring a big improvement, but I still may need caring for in the future. I know you will care for me, because I know how much you love me, and that thought is uppermost in my mind. But, I just feel that it will be such a burden on you.'

'The love I have for you, Pauline, is beyond all that. If it comes to it, I will look after you, without the slightest sense of it being a burden. You would do exactly the same for me, I know.'

The relief we both felt after that talk cleared away the tension that had been between us, and we did move on. Not every time we made love, after that, was a huge success, but that was probably much more to do with the fact that we were expecting far too much of ourselves, and let our desires take control of our rationale, and tried to be teenagers again. Our love life was as perfect as we would have wanted it to be, and I do not even qualify that by saying, 'considering our age,' because age did not come into it. We were old, not dead.

The release of tension made us feel that we needed to indulge in some concrete reminiscence therapy. We knew full well that trips into the past are dangerous, and we are well advised never to go back to places that linger, so happily, in the memory. We discussed it at great length, and both of us felt the need, and were willing to take the risk.

To go back to Scalford was, by far, the most difficult decision for Pauline to make, since the farm, her home at the time when she had suffered the most pain, was a place that she had never wanted to see again. But it was also the place of our beginning; a place that had seen us so happy.

The farmhouse was changed out of all recognition, having undergone extensive alterations, so did not register at all as the place that she had known as home. In the field by the house there were, appropriately, highland cattle, in recognition, we felt, of my new identity. 'Our meadow' was still as we had remembered it, and as we gazed upon it, in silent contemplation, Pauline moved to me, and as I held her I could feel the response to that memory moving through her body. Her eyes glistened, as they moistened, and we both lay in that grass together, in our silent remembrance.

The small town-centre of Melton Mowbray had changed very little, and, as we walked the streets, the memories of places and things came back to us with a warm glow. Crossing the bridge that led to the small public park was very different, in terms of the busy volume of traffic, heading out of town, but the park, itself, seemed just as we remembered it. We laughed, as we sat on the grass, and recalled the last time we had lain on that spot. Making our way to the river-side, we held hands, tightly, but we could see major changes there.

Most of the bushes had gone, from both sides of the river. We lay on the grass at the 'peeping-tom' spot. It would have been nice to make love, in memory, but had we done so we would undoubtedly have been arrested, since we were in full view of the people in the park, and pedestrians crossing the bridge.

Driving through the City of Leicester needed the sat-nav, as it was vastly different to how we knew it. Nothing remained that stirred the memory, but as we approached the village of Scraptoft the landscape became more familiar. There had been extensive building around the villages of Scraptoft and Thurnby, but none of that had obscured the places familiar to us. Even the alterations to my old home had not altered the character of the house, and we were able to recall, clearly and fondly the times we had spent in the place where we first made love, and where we became engaged, fifty eight years previously.

The fields were as we had walked through them, and we could believe that it was still the same grass, and we contemplated, together, that any rabbits there, (which we didn't see), were descended from those who had watched us, so long ago.

Those visits into the past meant so much to us that we went again, equally successfully, some time after we were married. There was no doubt that our past was very much a major part of our present.

That journey back into the past had taken just one day out of our lives, and at the end of that week, Gordon and Lili joined us in Chelmsford for an evening out with Pauline's best friend, and her husband, Lisa and Mark. Lisa told me that she had heard of me thirty years previously, when Pauline had told her of our teenage years together, and how hurt Pauline had been when I had dumped her.

'It was meant to happen,' said Lisa. She wasn't the first to say it, and she wouldn't be the last. ('It was meant to happen,' came from family members, Pauline's and mine; it came from friends; it came from casual aquaintances; it came from doctors and nurses in the hospitals and clinics where Pauline had appointments, where we were treated as celebrities, because Pauline never missed an opportunity to relate the 'magic tale', to all willing to listen). Pauline looked beautiful that evening, and, although I don't normally do pride, that evening, and every time I had Pauline by my side, I glowed with pride.

The physical change in her had been absolutely remarkable. I know it is a cliché but just being with Pauline made me feel like the luckiest man alive. Gordon and Lili were wonderful. Although I knew that they were delighted to see us together, I was still a little trepidatious about introducing my son to his prospective step-mother. I need not have worried; they loved each other from the start, and loquacious Lili saw Pauline as a girlfriend. Someone to share ideas with, about makeup, and fashion. Pauline's friends, who I was meeting for the first time, were astounded at the change in her. I'm not surprised, because she was radiant, and happiness shone out of both of us. The last time Gordon had seen me was at his mother's funeral, and the last time Pauline had seen her friend was to tell her about our disastrous meeting in June.

I did not want to go back to Spain, but on Friday, October 26th, at 7.30 am, I crossed the Channel with the motorbike, feeling that dichotomous sense of elation and dejection. It was October, and I was going back to Spain by the Millau Bridge, and through the Pyrenees.

The weather took care of my thinking very quickly, as it rained the kind of rain that seems unique to that part of France. The visibility was down to a few yards as the rain pounded on my visor, and the only way I could see where I was going was to fix myself to the tail-lights of a car in front.

French drivers do not hang about, so I was travelling, for most of the journey, at around 80 mph, praying that the car in front did not stop suddenly. My life had become very important to me, and my mortality was uppermost in my mind. Pauline did not like the bike; it was too big and too powerful for a little old guy like me, she said. Mindful of my new responsibilities, and surrendering to the desire to remain alive, I pulled off the road near Clermont Ferrand, and spent the night in a motel at Volcans. The weight of the water that had got through my leathers made it difficult to walk. I don't think I've ever been so pleased to get into a warm shower.

The following morning, when I arrived on the Mediterranean, southwest of Montpellier, it was so hot that I had to pull off the road and remove about two thirds of my clothing. The rain had stopped during the night, so the journey had become much more pleasant, and my mind had been occupied with Pauline, and plans for our future. I had told her that I didn't want us to just live together; I wanted us to be married. She said that she was very pleased that that was what I wanted, because she had been concerned about it, because it was what she wanted too, she said that it felt more like a real commitment. However, she said that it didn't have to be a big wedding.

'We could just get married in a Registry Office, and get a couple of witnesses in off the street,' she suggested.

I thought back to 1955, and the way she had looked forward to a wonderful wedding, and I knew that she would regret having had a 'hole-in-the-wall' wedding, when looking back to it from the future. She would always regret not having something to look back on with pleasure.

'No fear, my precious. A wedding is something special, even at our age. I want you to be a beautiful bride, getting a lot of love and admiration from all our friends. I want it to be a day that we can always look back on with pleasure, when we are old.'

In mid-November, I was going back home, to Scotland, with the bike, because it was due for its MOT. I just hoped that my car would be ready by then, because there was a lot of stuff that I needed to transport to Spain.

On November 14th I was out for a run near my house in Empuria. I tripped on a crooked bit of pavement; fell, and shattered the ring finger of my left hand. The hospital in Figueres cut off my old wedding ring, and put a huge plaster on my hand, extending almost to my elbow. (The ring was my wedding ring from when I was married to Rosemary, and was still on my finger because I had a swollen, arthritic knuckle, that prevented it from being removed, so there seemed to be something symbolic about its being cut off). Unfortunately, however, I was to take the bike back to Scotland for its MOT two days later.

I phoned Pauline from the hospital to tell her what had happened, and said that I would have to think of some way of getting the bike back. There was no way of operating the clutch lever on the bike with the plaster on, so I had only one choice – the plaster had to be removed. I soaked it in water and peeled it off, all the time thinking what I would have done to any patient of mine who had done that, when I was nursing. The finger was strapped to a metal splint, inside the plaster, and with a lot of sticking-plaster, I was able to retain the splint, and, with great difficulty, move the undamaged fingers enough to operate the clutch on the bike. I knew it was going to be a difficult journey, so I set off very early on the morning of November 16th. Going through the Pyrenees, it was snowing, but I was making very good time, so I decided to press on. When I arrived at Calais, my hand looked like a black haggis, the stretched skin shiny, and patched with different coloured blotches, and I could hardly move the fingers. The fingers were frozen into hooks, and they were completely unbendable, so for most of the way I had just hooked them over the clutch lever and pulled. It had been impossible to get a glove on, so the hand had been barely alive since I left Spain.

I phoned Pauline to tell her that I would be with her at around 2.00 am. I think she dropped the phone, and when I arrived at her house I dropped the bike. I just didn't have enough strength to hold it up any more.

A coffee; a snack; a lovely warm shower, and then we made love until the birds were singing. Not a comfortable time for my poor lady, though, with the end of a metal splint digging into her at every turn, and, as the life returned to my hand, with the warmth, it wasn't too great for me, either. But it was marvellous. The extra night I had gained had been well worth the suffering.

However, I think that that journey spelt the beginning of the end for my biking days. Pauline thought that it would be a good idea if I could stay alive, at least until the wedding, which we had set for April 10th 2013. But, in the meantime, I still had another long journey to do, up to Fife, to get the MOT done.

At least I got the car back when I was up in Scotland, which made it a much more comfortable journey back to Chelmsford. It was on Saturday, November 24th that we became engaged, and fixed our wedding date. Since I had taken Pauline's engagement ring away from her in 1955, I was determined that she would get another one. I had bought it in Roses, a town near where I was living in Spain, and it had been in my pocket, waiting for the right moment to give it to Pauline.

It was the evening of November, 24th that I went down on one knee to propose. I had to request that she didn't delay her answer too long, or I would need assistance to get up again. The first time we had become engaged I had got the ring size spot-on. This time, I didn't. The ring was a couple of sizes too big, and flopped about on her finger a little. Tearfully she accepted my proposal, and on the following Monday we got the ring cut to the right size.

During the next two weeks, we drove back up to Scotland, to introduce Pauline to my grandchildren, and my brother-in-law and his wife. On the way back south we called in to see Pauline's daughter, Sarah, in Penrith. The reception we received, from everyone, was wonderful. I had worried about going to see Peter and his wife, Pat.

I was mindful of the manner in which his sister, Margaret, had taken the news. It could not have been easy for any of Rosemary's family, because Rosemary had been dead for less than a year at that point. But there were no problems; no hostility, and no recriminations. In fact

Pauline was received with love, as I perceived it, as was I by Sarah. I did not take her to see Margaret, though.

I drove back to Spain on December 8th, only to fly back to Stansted on December 20th, to spend Christmas with Pauline.

CHAPTER 14

Nearly everyone I knew was aware that I was living in Spain, but very few of them knew my address, so I bought, and posted, all of my Christmas cards in Spain before I flew home for Christmas. That left me free to devote all of my time to Pauline, and doing my best to make it the happiest Christmas ever.

It was a time of the year that had so many memories for me, and a lot of them bad memories. I was looking forward so much to Christmas with Pauline, and I tried to think back to the last Christmas we had spent together, fifty eight years in the past, but, sadly, I could remember nothing of it. Pauline remembered little of it, also, except that she had bought me a leather cigarette case for a present, but her sister Dorothy had taken it, so I didn't get it.

The Christmas of 1955, however, I could never forget. I spent it in London, because my mother had thrown me out, because of what I had done to Pauline. It was the most miserable, cold, wet and lonely time I have ever had in my life, and now, in vivid contrast, I felt that I was headed for the warmest, most loving Christmas I could ever have wanted. It was to be a family Christmas, with Pauline's son, Alex, and his wife Mimi, coming from their home in Hounslow, to spend a few days with us.

It would be my first meeting with Alex and Mimi, and we were to spend many hours telling them of our past, and sharing Alex's childhood memories, and of the times when he and his sister, Sarah, had been with their mother to visit my mother.

I reminded Pauline that it was the revelation of those visits they had made to my mother in Leicestershire, that prompted me to search for her. It had been at Christmastime that my sister had told me about it.

Pauline asked me if Christmas Day would be painful for me, because, though it was to be our 'real' first together, it was the first anniversary of Rosemary's death, and my last Christmas with Rosemary.

'No, my love,' I told her.' My memories of Rosemary are good ones, not sad ones, and I can look back with pleasure. My life, now, is ahead of me, not behind me, and you are my life. I don't want to look back, with sadness, I want to look forward, to the wonderful life that we will be sharing together.'

It was true, I did not want to dwell on the previous Christmas, and Rosemary's dying, but Christmas is a time for reflection, and it was impossible not to think about it. There was also a touch of discomfort, too. I was embarking on a new beginning, with Pauline, and there was a feeling of guilt, that it was such a huge leap in such a short time.

Pauline and I were so happy, and all of the simple domesticity of Christmas gave us such pleasure. Just decorating a Christmas tree together, along with the choosing, and buying, and wrapping of presents. On Boxing Day, Gordon and Lili came to us for the day. It was a happy mingling of our two families, and it was wonderful to see everyone getting on so warmly. Gordon and Lili loved Pauline very much, and I know it pleased Alex and Mimi to see Pauline so happy.

That Christmas had meant so much to us, and when I left, for Spain, on January 3rd, it was quite a wrench, but Pauline was flying out to Spain on January 17th, just two weeks away. Also, our wedding was only twelve weeks away, and although I was in Spain for most of that time, leaving Pauline to do the donkey work of the arrangements, we were in very close touch. I phoned her twice a day, and we 'Skyped' on a daily basis too.

Pauline's stay with me in January saw us enjoying beautiful weather, and I have many photographs of that holiday. By that time she had undergone a complete metamorphosis, and when I look at the pictures of her at that time, and compare them with the ones I had taken in the 'miserable June,' it is not possible to believe that it is the same person. It was wonderful to see her so radiantly happy. I had made a lot of friends in Spain, since I had gone out there, and I relished the task of introducing Pauline to them.

It was a wonderfully relaxing, idyllic time together, with long walks along the beaches, by the Mediterranean, bathed in glorious sunshine; palm trees; sandy beaches, and eating out nightly, in great restaurants. We went into France, and shopped in Perpignan; we drove through the snowy Pyrenees, and visited Andorra.

When we looked in shop windows, I would ask her,

'Do you like that?'

'I'm not going to tell you, because you would buy it for me. You spoil me.'

'Of course I spoil you. I love spoiling you. Now, which one do you want?'

We laughed a lot and we loved a lot, and the whole experience was magical, beyond anything we could ever have dreamed of.

On the day she flew home, we drove to Barcelona on a magnificent evening, and as the sun went down the whole sky was a glorious red. We spoke little, and we held hands for most of the way. I felt her happy sadness through her fingers, and I knew she was crying. At one point, the car radio played Jennifer Rush, singing 'The Power of Love,' and Pauline gripped hold of my arm, and I heard her sobbing as she buried her face into my shoulder. (It was one of the songs that was later played at our wedding). I remembered, so vividly, when she had told me that she had no emotions. The 'ice-queen,' she had called herself.

Mid-February, I had to fly home for an appointment with the Registrar in Cupar, to obtain a 'Certificate of No Impediment,' to prove that Rosemary was dead, and that I was free to marry. Pauline had to get copies of her divorce papers, from somewhere in London, since her original ones had been lost. These acts were not without some reflection, and put us in a context that we had been free of for the time we had been planning our wedding, and we were reminded where we had previously been, and of the life we had been living for many years before we got to that new stage.

On that visit home, we also arranged our wedding venue; sent out the invitations, and bought me a suit. I hadn't worn a suit for many years, and the only one I had was well out of date; an altered seventies one. I would have prefered to wear my kilt, but Pauline said that that would have been fine if we were marrying in Scotland. (Later, when she saw me in the kilt, she said she wished I had worn it for our wedding).

The next time I was home was for the final arrangements, and the wedding. Preparing for the wedding together was exhilarating, and we scampered about, doing things with frenzied animation. Pauline had already chosen what she wanted to wear, and I was just along with her to confirm her choice before purchase. I sat, with a huge lump in my throat, as she decided to try on several dresses, and hats. But, as could have been predicted, she went with her original choice. The dress was a purplish navy colour, with large print flowers down the front. It was to be worn with a short purple jacket, purple shoes and a purple 'satellite dish' for a hat. (Guess what her favourite colour was). I also gave her a Swarovski crystal necklace for a wedding present, and it looked perfect with her outfit.

Walking away from the cash-point, I put my arm around her and she smiled up at me as I kissed her. A few steps later she stopped. Pauline looked up at me, and with an almost detached air, she asked, 'are you really happy Glenn?'

'Of course I am, aren't you?' There was too long a hesitation before she replied, from a distance, I thought,

'Yes, I'm really happy, but......I want your babies!'

I was startled. 'Yes...Right...I really wish that could be possible, my love, but I think we have used up more than our fair share of miracles over this last few months, don't you?' I noticed then that we were walking through the children's department. I felt the need too, and it set my head in a spin as I remembered the times we had talked about 'our children,' how many we would have, what names we would give them.

'I know, but I loved you so much Glenn, and I so looked forward to us being married, and bringing up a family. I have Alex and Sarah, and I love them with all my heart. They were what kept me sane during the 'bad' years, but I just wish you and I could have had children. We laughed about that peeping-tom, remember, but when I got home that day I lay on my bed and I just cried and cried. I wanted to be pregnant more than anything in the world. I'm sorry, I'm just being daft. Let's go and get a coffee before we go to the jewellers.'

'We wanted four children, my love, and we have three between us, so let's just recognise that they are 'our' kids, and with no nappies or snotty noses to bother about.'

Pauline laughed, and we got the escalator up a couple of floors to the cafeteria, and coffee and maple syrop and pecan plaits.

The jewellers did not have a wedding ring that would fit over my arthritic knuckle, so it had to be ordered.'

'The wedding is next week, how long will it take to come in?'

'No problem, it will be in tomorrow or the day after,' replied the very cheery assistant, 'but I'll mark it as urgent, just to make sure.'

We deliberately made it, very much, a combined family affair. Gordon was my Best Man; Sarah made our wedding cake, and my stepson, Alex, did the photographs.

Pauline said that she had practised writing 'Pauline Spiers', as her signature in 1955, because she had wanted it so much, and she felt that she was in a dream now that it was really happening. (I recently found an old notebook of hers, with a full page of 'Pauline M Spiers' practise signatures in it, that she had been practising again since we had come back together).

On the morning of the wedding, Pauline and I went to the hotel where it was to be, to meet with some of our guests, who had travelled, and were staying there. We had friends who had come down from Fife, and Rosemary's brother, Peter and his wife had come down all the way from Lossiemouth. It was wonderful that these people had travelled so far, just to be with us on our glorious day, and it made us feel very special.

It was a small venue, because it was a small wedding, with just twenty seven very close guests from friends and family, but the hotel was perfect for our needs. It had a separate room especially for such occasions, and it was very intimate and friendly. Most of the guests were 'mature' so there were no wedding drunks or family fights, or children running wild, spilling drinks. In fact, people who arrived complete strangers left, old friends, having come together very quickly.

The only disappointment was, no Richard. He hadn't replied to the invitation, and Pauline said, 'that's Richard. I'm not surprised.'

But I was disappointed because Richard had played a part, as the 'go-between' in our getting back together.

(Two weeks later we did get a reply from Richard, saying how much he was looking forward to being at our wedding on 10th May). Good old Richard; right date wrong month!

Pauline had emailed me, when I was in Spain, with her choice of music for the ceremony. She suggested 'When I fall in Love,' by Nat King Cole for our entrance; 'Nights in White Satin,' The Mooy Blues, (sic), during the signing of the Register, and 'The Power of Love,' Jennifer Rush, for the leaving. Nat King Cole; a great choice, I thought, and 'The Power of Love,' was essential, but I wasn't too sure about the 'bovine' group, 'The 'Mooy' Blues.

We had never spent any 'nights in white satin,' and I couldn't imagine us ever being 'satiny' people. Going through my own collection, I came across 'Right Down the Line,' by Gerry Rafferty. Pauline had never heard it, so I sent her a copy, and she loved it. It was a bit 'my side,' but Pauline was happy with that because she had thought that the Jennifer Rush had been very 'her side.' Sorry, Moody Blues.

We drove to the venue in my car, and when we alighted, at the hotel, disaster struck. Pauline was wearing hold-up stockings, and they weren't holding up. When she stood up on leaving the car her legs were doing an excellent 'Nora Batty' impression, like spindled concertinas. She disappeared rapidly into the toilet, before anyone saw her, while I paid a visit to reception to beg a couple of rubber bands, which caused a lot of amusement among the hotel staff.

For two days before the wedding, it rained, and we were expecting rain again on the day of the wedding, but, as we arrived at the venue, the sun came out. The symbolism was striking, and commented on by many, and the sun remained out for the rest of the day, until it set in the evening. It then rained all night. We spent the night at Canterbury, to be reasonably close to the ferry port, for an early start.

Beyond the wedding we had our honeymoon back in Spain, and apart from the fact that we were driven off the road near Paris, on our return home after the honeymoon, and almost killed, we began life as newlyweds. On May 16th we moved to my house in Fife, on the agreement that we would sell up as soon as we could, and move to England. We both agreed that we needed a completely fresh start, with no 'baggage.' A home in Spain was seriously considered, but, although the Spanish health care system is marvellous, we could not get a seamless transfer, and that would have been absolutely essential.

A buyer was found, very quickly, for the cottage, and we spent hours poring over internet sites, looking for somewhere to live in Leicestershire. We had decided to return to our roots. About half a dozen prospective purchases were listed, and I made a reservation at a motel for a week, so that we could go and view the properties. Three days before we were to go down to England, something happened.

Pauline was standing in the kitchen, staring out of the window. I quietly moved up behind her and slipped my arms around her waist. She put her hands and arms over mine, and moved her head back against my face as I buried my nose in the silver nimbus of her hair behind her right ear.

'A penny for them,' I whispered.

'Nothing, I was just thinking about things.'

We stared, silently out of the window, together, and I knew what she meant. I was much more familiar with that view than she was, having seen it for thirty years, but I had never taken it for granted. It was a view north to the distant misty Perthshire hills, and on a clear, frosty winter's day the snow capped tops of the Cairngorms could be seen. It was different every time I looked out, and I never stopped loving it. In the immediate foreground was the back lawn and drying green, beyond which was the well planted vegetable garden. The fields then sloped down a long way to the St Andrews road before rising towards the horizon of mountains. There must have been twenty or thirty goldfinches, at the bird-feeding station, to the left of the lawn, fluttering impatiently from place to place, twittering loudly, flashing gold wings, or perched, swaying precariously, on the very tips of the spindly branches of an apple tree, or surrounding shrubs. Blue tits and great tits were busy at the peanut feeders, and coal tits darted out from the bushes and back again with some morsel they had grabbed.

'Thank you, Glenn. Thank you for looking for me, and for loving me. You have made me so happy; I know just how lucky I am.'

'How lucky we are,' I corrected her.

'When I told my friend and neighbour, Maureen, that you had searched for me on the internet, she said, "that's fantastic, I can't think of anything more brilliantly romantic, you must feel like a millionaire." I felt much more than that Glenn, I can't describe just how I felt.'

'I set out to find you once, did I tell you?' she said.

'What? When? No you didn't tell me. Where was I? Was it recently?'

'No, no, it was a long time ago, before you were married. Your mother had just told me that you were stationed at HMS Ganges, near Ipswich, just a bus-ride away from Chelmsford. I was in town with Alex, he was two, and I was very pregnant with Sarah. I was at a very low ebb at that point, and I thought about you a lot. I needed you Glenn, I really needed you. I felt so lonely. I was passing the bus station, and I decided, right on the spur of the moment, to get a bus to try and find you. We went across to the stance, and when a bus came in we got on. I sat staring out of the window, trying to think what I would do when I got there. I imagined being at the main gate at Ganges, with someone phoning the sick bay to tell you I was there. "A young lady, very pregnant and with a two-year-old boy." I imagined your face, then I knew what a stupid idea it was. I scrambled out of the seat and shuffled

Alex along the passageway. The driver had just got into his seat, and the conductor was just about to come up the steps onto the bus. "Excuse me. I'm sorry," I mumbled as we almost fell down the steps.

I stood on the platform and wept as the bus pulled away. I think that was the first time I realised that I would never see you again, so you can see what it means to me to be with you now, can't you.'

I stayed silent. There was nothing I could think of to say. I just pulled her closer to me and held her tight.

'What would you have done?'

'About what?'

'What would you have done if I had gone through with it? Would you have come to the gate to see me?'

'I can't get myself there Pauline; I don't know what I would have done. Yes, I think I would have gone to the gate to see you, but I think I would have been quite upset, seeing you there pregnant, and with Alex at your hand. I might even have been angry. It wouldn't have had a happy ending, Pauline.'

'That's what I thought at the time, so I'm glad I didn't do it. I regretted not going for ages after though. I wanted you to know the truth; to know that I hadn't betrayed you. If you'd accepted me then, Glenn, I would have left John for you. I've no doubt about it.'

The goldfinches suddenly took off, en masse, from the bird-feeders, a glittering charm, dispersing into the bushes, as a greater-spotted woodpecker landed on one of the peanut feeders. As the woodpecker circled its way around the feeder, with a staccato stabbing of its needle beak into the nuts, the Goldfinches quickly regained their courage, and returned to the feeders and perches. The Perthshire hills were hazy, curving shades of blue in the far distance.

We had fallen silent again.

'I don't want to go, Glenn.'

'Don't want to go where?'

'I don't want to live in England...I want to stay in Scotland. I've come home, Glenn. I always wanted to be home, and now I'm here. I'm happy beyond anything that I could ever have expected. Thank God you found me. Thank God you were able to get past my silliness, and come back for me. I think we should find another house, to start over, but I never want to leave Scotland now. It's my home. It's where I was always meant to be, with you.'

I couldn't believe what I was hearing. 'Is this because of me? Do you just want to stay in Scotland now because of me?' I asked her. 'You really don't need to do that Pauline. As long as we are together, I don't care where we live. You know that I am already settled to the idea of living in Leicestershire. My sister lives there, and we would be much closer to Alex and Mimi, in London. It has so many memories for us, and I'm certain that we would be perfectly happy there.'

'No Glenn, that's not it. I didn't think I would like it here because I would feel like a foreigner. I wouldn't know anybody, and I thought I would be lonely. But I'm not a stranger here. I really feel as if I've always lived here. Everyone we know has made such a fuss of me, even just people in shops, cafes and the doctor's surgery; people I would never have known back in Chelmsford know me by name here, and greet me like a friend. I had to phone the Health Centre the other day to make an appointment to see the doctor, and do you know what the receptionist said?'

'No, what did she say?'

'She said, "I'm sorry, but I'm afraid you won't be able to see a doctor until this afternoon, Mrs Spiers, is that alright?"'

'Well maybe they were busy.' I apologised.

'No, you don't understand what I'm saying. The receptionist back at the surgery in Chelmsford wouldn't even have known my name, even though I had been registered there for over thirty years, and I would have been lucky to get an appointment in the same month, let alone the same day. When you first took me to the surgery to register, the practice nurse saw me in her office. She gave me a hug and told me that she hoped that you and I would be really happy together. She talked to me about you and Rosemary, and said that she was so happy for us, because you deserved some happiness. She wasn't just a nurse, Glenn, she was a friend. I love it here. It's a beautiful place. Just a short drive away, and we are in the mountains, and I've never seen such beautiful scenery in my life, and it's right on our doorstep.'

'So, what happened to the city girl, 'through and through,' desperate for shops and people?'

'Yes, OK, I know I said that. I also know that I said that I would never leave Chelmsford, but I'm here, aren't I? I just wanted to claim to be like that to get up your nose, you know that, but I am a country girl. I know I am. I was anonymous in the city. No-one knew me, apart from friends, and that was what I wanted. I didn't want to be anybody, because I didn't have anything to be anybody about. I want people to know me now, and they do, and they know our story, and it's marvellous. I want the whole world to know me, because now I'm somebody.'

'OK, if that's what you want. Are you really sure?'

I can't say that I wasn't pleased. I thought back to my first time in Scotland, and how the country had grown on me, and I could understand, perfectly, why she felt as she did.

It was back to internet searching, and after viewing around half a dozen houses, we saw a house in Alyth, in Perthshire, that Pauline loved.

' I knew it was the one as soon as we went into it,' she said, 'didn't you feel that?'

What I remembered most was a giant black labradoodle, which spent most of the viewing time sniffing at bits of me that I would have preferred not to have sniffed.

But, I did like it; better than all the others we had seen. 'If that's the one you want, then that's the one we'll get,' I replied. We went for a meal at a hotel by the Alyth Burn, and then had a look round the place. It really did look like a very attractive little town; more like a large village, than a town, but we did like it, and we never regretted moving there, on February 5th, 2014.

Three weeks after our move, we flew to New Zealand, for the wedding of Pauline's grandson, Alan. He and his

New Zealand wife, Christine, lived in Queenstown, South Island, and it was the furthest Pauline had ever travelled in her life. I had sold the motorbike, to raise the money for our fares, and after a wonderful holiday, we returned home, excitedly setting about our new life together, in our new house. We were blissfully happy, as we created our garden together, and did all of the things that always need doing in a new house. Old, we may have been, but we were no different to any other newly married couple, setting up home. Incidently, we still had Maisie, and she also loved Scotland, and the wide open spaces. She was seventeen years old then, and found a new lease of life, catching field-mice, and chasing birds, a town cat no longer.

It was in May, 2014, that Pauline first noticed it. Pauline was sitting at her dressing table, putting on her makeup, when she called me over.

'Come and look at this,' Pauline said.

'Come and look at what?'

'It's a lump. Come and see what you think.'

That was just three months after we had moved to Alyth. The lump was quite small, above her right eye. I looked at it, and ran my fingers over her forehead and scalp. There was one on her scalp too. There also appeared to be one on her neck, just below her left ear, but that may have been auto-suggestion, because I was worried that there might be one there. There was no way of knowing what the lumps were, so I told her that she would have to see the doctor.

'I'm seeing Dr Lin, in Perth, in a couple of days' time. I will tell her about them.'

Dr Lin was the rheumatologist, and had been looking after Pauline's treatment since we had moved to Perthshire. Other lumps had appeared on her head, and other parts of her body, and the one I had thought I had found on her neck had definitely developed, and we began to worry. When we saw Dr Lin, she said that the lumps could be related to Pauline's arthritis, but she would refer her to a haematologist, just to check them out.

Pauline saw Mr Mitchelson quite quickly, and on June 5th she had a biopsy done on the lump that had come up on her neck. In fact the whole lymph gland was removed.

Several other lumps had appeared, and Pauline and I were both experienced enough to be deeply worried. We had a good idea what the diagnosis would be, and we were proved right on June 25th, when she was told that she had Non-Hodgkins Lymphoma – Lymphatic Cancer.

I said nothing, and Pauline remained quiet too. I took her into my arms, and held her tight, wiping away the small tears that had welled in her eyes.

From that moment on, our lives seemed to enter a vacuum, and we went through the motions of living, in slow motion. We were stunned. We were hurt. We were frightened. Our whole existence had suddenly become porcelain fragile.

Pauline and I cherished every moment of our lives from then on. Our mortality had become stark.

'We are looking at this as very curable,' said Mr Mitchelson. 'You are not just getting palliative care, we are treating this to cure it,' he continued. 'Now, because of your existing conditions, we are going to have to discuss the way forward, in the team. I want to talk to the rheumatologist, to get her view. I'd like you to come back in two days time, and by then we will know what we are proposing.'

It was difficult to take this in, but we were aware that his voice was positive, not sympathetic.

Mr Mitchelson phoned us the following morning, early, and asked us to go in at 11.00 am the following day. I was worried about the seeming urgency, and I questioned him about it, but he said that they had been able to reach a decision more quickly than he had expected, and there was nothing to worry about. They just felt that it would be better to get on with the treatment as soon as possible.

'The ideal would have been to treat you with radiotherapy, and chemotherapy,' said Mr Mitchelson, the following day, 'but, unfortunately, because of the pulmonary fibrosis, it's not worth the risk, so we are going to put you on a course of chemo called a mini-CHOP. The CHOP is the initials of the drugs used in the 'cocktail,' and it is a 'mini', because, again, your condition would not allow for a full-CHOP. It will be just as effective, however, and we have every confidence that you will make a full recovery.' He really was very reassuring, and Pauline smiled, and squeezed my hand. 'We must do a bone-marrow biopsy, first, to further the diagnosis,' Mr Mitchelson continued, 'and I'm afraid that that will be a bit sore. Sorry.'

The biopsy indicated that the lymphoma was high-grade, which Mr Mitchelson said was good news, as the treatment would be more positively specific.

We knew that Pauline would lose her hair, and she made an appointment to be fitted for a wig. We laughed about that, and made jokes about her being bald. We would be a matching pair. We had to do some laughing, just to keep alive, but there was always a hollowness to it.

It was at that fitting that the whole import of what was happening hit Pauline. She was very fussy about her hair since she and I got back together, and had grown it from the 'short back and sides' of June 2012, (that I used to call her 'cell block H style'), and, grey though it was, it was very attractive. As she discussed it with the hairdresser, the tears came, and I felt so wretchedly helpless. All I could do was hold her, and I did a lot of that.

There would be a course of six chemotherapy sessions, once every three weeks. Each session would last about three hours, and we were warned that there could be unpleasant side-effects. I was able to stay with her throughout the duration of the treatment, and that pleased me greatly, and Pauline.

The first one was on August 5th.

Pauline responded well to the chemotherapy. When her hair started to fall out in large quantities, Pauline decided to have her head shaved. I did it for her, and it was a terrible moment, for both of us. The wig, she did not like, and wore it very rarely. It was too hot for her, and, anyway, she looked very beautiful without it, and I loved that shaved head.

Pauline was still very sexy to me, and the chemo did not diminish her libido. We had been warned that we should take care, as I could end up sharing her treatment. I'm afraid that I may well have shared the treatment, anyway, because we continued our love life as we had always done. I didn't really care; and why not share that, we shared everything else.

Because the chemo destroyed her natural immunity, we had to be very careful that she kept free of infection. Her temperature was taken at least twice a day, and because it became elevated a couple of times, Pauline had to be admitted for observation. A third time, however, was more serious, because she had a chest infection, which did not respond well to antibiotics, and it took some time to bring it under control.

That was in November, just after her 5th chemotherapy treatment. She was in hospital for two weeks, and on November 14th, Pauline was told that the chemotherapy treatment had exacerbated her pulmonary fibrosis, and the sixth treatment would not be administered. Mr Mitchelson insisted that this would not jeopardise her recovery. But she was left with quite a bad cough, and that worried us.

On November 15th, I was able to take some good cheer into the hospital to Pauline, with a photograph, taken from an email from the other side of the world, of her twin great-grandchildren, a boy and a girl, Ruri and Isla, who were born in New Zealand at 13.00, UK time, that day. I think most of the staff in the hospital got to see the pictures. Well, the ones who had been party to 'our story,' anyway.

Pauline was quite weak when she was discharged from hospital on November 18th, and we had a very quiet time, to let her strength build up. We had also decided that we wanted a very relaxed, and quiet Christmas that year, on our own, and we arranged to go and stay in Vallauris, near Antibes, in the South of France. My nephew has a small holiday home there. I think it was a good move, really, because she did seem to improve.

Into the New Year, all the tests she had showed Pauline to be in full remission, and she was definitely getting stronger. Her hair was growing, and the world was opening up for her again, and we gradually became more active.

It was our second wedding anniversary on April 10th, and I wanted to do something special for the occasion. Pauline loved the highland area around Glencoe, and the road to Inverness, so I booked three nights at the inn at The Falls of Dockart; a place that she was particularly fond of. We did a lot of travelling, in that three days, and Pauline loved every moment of it, and felt that it had been very therapeutic.

The stress of those months, since her diagnosis, had been intense. Pauline had wanted to go to Malta, ever since we had got back with each other, because it was one of the places where we would have been together, if we had married, back in 1957, the year we first planned to be married. She just wanted to see what it would have been like. I booked a ten day holiday in a five star hotel in Valletta, to celebrate her birthday, which was on May 22nd.

We flew out to Malta on May 20th. Pauline was still quite frail, and used a walking stick, and because of that the airline arranged for us to be met by a courier, when we changed flights in Germany, and we were whisked to our next terminal in an electric transporter, feeling very VIP.

I had hired a car in Malta, and for the first few days we got around quite a lot, but the last three days we spent, mostly, in and around the hotel, because Pauline became quite tired. By the final day, she was looking forward to being home.

We left Malta on Saturday, May 30th, and after we landed at Heathrow, we were picked up by Alex, and we spent the night at his house in Hounslow, where I had left our car before we had flown out to Malta.

We drove home to Scotland on the Sunday, calling in by Sarah's, in Penrith, on the way north. Sarah commented that Pauline did not look well, and she was right. Pauline was frail, and tired. But we expected that, after the travelling we had done.

We had a meal, on the way home, so that no cooking would be required when we arrived. It was a bar-meal, in a pub in a little village called Crook-of-Devon. That was a regular stop-off for us on the way home. The landlord had always remembered us, from the very first time I had taken Pauline in there, and it was so good to get his friendly greeting. (Though he didn't know it, it was his friendliness that went a long way towards persuading Pauline that she wanted to live in Scotland).

It was good to be home, and we relaxed, before an early bed, and Pauline 'unwound.' It was lovely to be in our own bed again, and we both felt it.

It was just after 4.00 am that Pauline woke me to say that she felt peculiar.

'I think I'm dying, Glenn, she said.' And she was very frightened. She meant what she was saying, and I felt that icy hand clutch at my heart.

I took her temperature. It was a little raised, but not worryingly so, but I phoned NHS 24. The paramedics arrived very quickly, at around 4.30. Pauline's SATS were very low, at less than 50. The reading should have been in the high 90's, which meant that her blood/oxygen level was very low. She was taken into Ninewells Hospital, and admitted to the High Dependency Unit, mostly because of the level of oxygen that she needed.

Pauline became much calmer, because she was in hospital, and could receive emergency treatment without any problem. The urgency for action over, I was able to hold her in my arms, and comfort her. The oxygen helped her enormously, and her breathing improved, and she slept.

Later that day, after I had been home and freshened up, I went back to the hospital, to learn that Pauline had pneumonia. Normally, very treatable, in her case it was not so straightforward, because of her recent chemotherapy history, and because of her pulmonary fibrosis, but after several different antibiotics, she started to respond to treatment. Over two litres of fluid was aspirated from her lungs, and her breathing became almost normal.

On Thursday June 4th, I was with her in the hospital when a doctor told her that she would probably be transferred to a general ward the following day, prior to discharge. It seemed that the infection had cleared, and she was on the way to full recovery. I knew she was much better because she was getting very impatient to be home.

In the late afternoon we were holding hands, and

talking about the things that would need to be done when she got home, when she pulled me to her and kissed me.

'I love you so much, Glenn,' she said, 'I hate being away from you.' She pulled me closer and said, 'you are so good to me, I don't know how I would have coped with this without you. I wish you could get in bed with me.'

'That might cause a bit of a stir, I think. Not too practical, either, you're catheterised.'

'I don't care if it would cause a stir. I want you near me, Glenn, I miss you so much. The catheter is no problem. I could easily get that out of the way. Come on, pull the curtains around the bed.' She laughed, and it was so good to hear that laugh. It seemed a long time since laughter had been in our lives, and it was, normally, such a big part of us. I left her that night feeling much springier in my step, looking forward to her being home. I planned to take her somewhere really special, to celebrate. Pauline loved going out.

The phone by my bed rang. It was around 3.30 am.

If a phone rings at 3.30 am, it is going to be urgent, and that ring, at that time sounded very urgent. Before I answered it my heart was racing, because I knew what it was likely to be.

'Mr Spiers?'

'Yes!'

'Mr Spiers, this is the duty nurse in HDU. I am sorry, but I think you should come in.'

'Is she dying?' I gasped. I was already out of bed, and throwing my clothes on.

'It doesn't look too good. Pauline is having very great difficulty breathing.'

'I'll be there as quickly as I can. Please tell Pauline that I love her, and I'll be there as fast as I can make it.'

The drive in was a nightmare; like a hideous dream. The whole world was dead. It was the middle of the night. Why was it so unnaturally bright? It should be dark. It should always be dark now, and never be daylight again. 'Macbeth hath murdered sleep.'

Everywhere was so quiet; no movement; no people. Was everybody dead? No cars. I looked at my watch; time was still moving, but every tick was now in the past. My watch is electronic, why can I hear it ticking? Traffic-lights were alive. Why do they go red, when there is no-one there to observe them? Trees crashed soundlessly to the ground in the forests, because there was no-one there to hear them. For Christ's sake, will somebody turn off the daylight, its blinding me.

Normally a 30 minute drive, I was there in just over 20 minutes.

Miracle of miracles, the hospital car parks were empty. I had to get a parking ticket. Why should I have to pay now? I'm not alive. You shouldn't have to pay when you are dead.

The hospital was dead. I think there was somebody at the enquiry desk, but he was dead. All of the shop units were dead. I could not stop and browse the books on the second-hand book stall, each book a pound, to go into the hospital ammenity fund, because there were no books there.

Why are there so many damn stairs?

Am I still moving? I can't get to where I want to get to. I seem to be going all over the hospital, and my objective is slipping further away from me all the time.

I wish I'd had time to stop and buy her some flowers.

As soon as I broke through the curtains around her bed, I knew that I was too late. She was dead; I was dead. She had died alone; I had died alone.

That has been the one thing that has haunted me ever since; my Pauline died alone. I know there were nurses there, but that is not the same as me being there.

As I fell forwards, towards the bed, I gave out a cry, and the two nurses grabbed me and stopped me collapsing to the floor. I steadied myself and I took Pauline in my arms, and I could do nothing but cry. She was warm; she didn't look dead. She couldn't be dead. I begged her to wake up.

'I'm here now pet. Please wake up. Please wake up. I love you, Pauline. Please don't leave me.'

I wished I could die there and then, in some perverse belief that I would be with her. I wanted to be with her. I kissed her over and over, and I pleaded with her not to be dead.

'Please, she can't be dead,' I beseeched the nurse, 'we have only been married two years. It's just not fair. Please tell me that she isn't dead.'

But it was hopeless. Pauline was dead. I was dead. I was in utter despair; desolate, and I knew that I could never be helped.

Pauline had died about ten minutes before I arrived, at 4.10 am, on June 5th.

I left the bed with the nurse's arm about my waist, to keep me steady. I had phoned Sarah, before I left the house, and she would be on her way up, with her partner, Bruce. I called her mobile, and I heard her voice stick, and the sob, as she said that they would be with me as soon as possible.

'How are you?' asked Sarah. 'Will you be OK?'

'Yes, Sarah, I'll be alright. Please take your time, and take care. I'll wait here, in the hospital until you arrive.'

'Bruce will have to leave me there, with you, because he has to work, and he'll have to turn right around and drive back to Penrith.'

'That's no problem, Sarah. Will you stay with me until everything is over, please?'

'Of course I will. We'll be able to do everything that needs to be done together.'

The dead world was moving again, I think, as I waited for Sarah in the foyer. People were talking, but there was no sound. I was glad that they were showing such respect. All of their faces showed sadness.

I remembered once thinking that I never wanted to enter Ninewells Hospital again.

EPILOGUE

As I walked, silently, to the car with Sarah, it felt as if we were under water. The light had a sterile, phosphorescent glow to it, and people were moving slowly, and silently, and they had no definable shapes.

The drive home was surreal. It was too practical. I had to do things, and see things, and look at things, and that did not seem right, but there was still no sound, even when Sarah spoke.

The house was emptier than it had ever been. It was so dead, and cold, but Maisie was there, demanding to be fed. I had forgotten that Maisie wasn't dead. I can't remember seeing her when I had left the house. She didn't show any sign that she knew what had happened. Pauline had cared for her for seventeen years, and Maisie would never see her again, but Maisie never indicated that she was aware of that.

That tick that I had heard from my watch was still in my head, but louder, from the clocks in the house, counting my life into the past. Everything is in the past now. The journey to the hospital; the ward where she had lain, so still; the journey home; all in the past now. Tomorrow; next week; next year are all back in the past now, from whence I had taken them. I had reached back into the past and brought it into the present, and given it a future. But it was an illusion. Every moment we live becomes, instantly, a part of the past, and it can't be brought back. The pain of that awful three days we had had, back in 'that June,' was the battle against the 'invisible force' that was trying to prevent us from wrenching the past through the barrier that separates us from what has been. It was as if what we were trying to do was unnatural; a sin against some unwritten law of the universe; a third Mortal Sin? I had a 'full-house' now, – missing Mass on Sundays, murder, and now, trying to control and manipulate time and fate. I had committed them all, and I could feel the flames of Hell licking at my feet. We have been made to pay for my sins by having our future snatched from us and cast into the past.

Even now my death is in the past. I just have to catch up with it, that's all.

I felt, suddenly, so hideously filthy. I had left the house without washing, or even combing my hair. My mouth was swollen with filth, and I had to go and clean my teeth and shower, quickly.

'It's Friday,' said Sarah, 'and we've a lot to do before the weekend.'

'The Alyth Voice,' our local free publication, came into its own, as we sought the details we needed for the Registrar, the Funeral Director and the florist.

Between us, Sarah and I phoned all of the people that needed to be informed, and we made appointments. I went to my laptop and composed a notice of Pauline's death, and the funeral notice, and placed the printed off copies into the addressed envelopes. I tried to imagine the faces of our friends, who had been so happy for us just two years back, when they got the notification that we were no more.

None of what we were doing seemed real. The Registrar, the Funeral Director and the florist were all suitably saddened, and expressed their sympathy, and I know that they meant it.

We went into Marks and Spencer in Perth, and ordered trays of food, to be collected, for the gathering, on the day of the funeral. They weren't sad. They probably thought it was for a happy occasion.

Pauline was cremated, at Perth Crematorium, on Thursday, June 11th, 2015.

I placed a posy of bluebells, that I had picked that morning in the Den o' Alyth, with the wreaths on the lid of the coffin, and I let my hand linger there. I closed my eyes and relaxed as the long grass gently rustled about my head in the gentle breeze. The smell of the earth, and the faint fungus scent of mushrooms filled my nostrils, and I could see the waving heads of the meadow flowers about us. I so wanted to hold her in my arms, but the train was pulling away from the station. I let her slide gently from my grasp onto the platform. 'I love you Pauline. I love you so much.'

I had been reminded, gently, but firmly, that my eulogy was to be twenty minutes, and not a moment longer, because we were on the conveyer belt of a 'deduction' line. Henry Ford in reverse. Thank God Pauline was with me to give me strength.

On Sunday, June 14th, Gordon, the last of the family to leave, went home, and I was on my own, with Pauline all around me, huge, in her absence, from her chair, and her kitchen.

Her place in our bed had been empty for a few days, since she had gone into the hospital, but it was much emptier now, as the presence of her absence became so tangible. With the house being full, over the days of the funeral, I had surrendered my bed to Sarah, and slept on a camp-bed in the office. It was some days before I could return to our empty bed again.

When I was eighteen, and I first met Pauline, on that train, I felt I was only just being born; my life began then, as far as I was concerned. We were so young, and we had our lives planned. We knew exactly where we were going, and felt that nothing could stand in our way, and we learned, the hard way, that life may seem to be ours to own, but it is not ours to control.

We had done it again. Again we had believed that our happiness, and the strength of our love had put us back in control of our lives again. We were invincible; indestructable; to live forever.

'I am so happy, Glenn. I don't think I have ever been so happy,' Pauline had said. 'I feel much better than I have felt for such a long time. I'm sure my health has improved a lot, since we got back together.'

We believed it, so it must have been true.

Of course I was devastated, when I lost Pauline, and in the absolute depths of despair. I was bereft, and utterly miserable, and why the hell shouldn't I be? We had been cheated; robbed of the wonderful life that we deserved. Two years and eight weeks was not enough. Yes, I know there are millions of people who are much worse off than me, and I resented them all. They made me feel worse, not better, because they made me feel guilty, absorbed, as I was, with my troubles, when thousands were dying all over the world.

I am also guilty of being a fully paid up member of 'the ageing population,' subject to the constant subliminal barrage from the Government, and the BBC, that I am responsible for all of the ills of society, and should do the patriotic thing, and move on into that final dimension, and as soon as possible.

There are times in your life when your existence is thrust full in your face. It is then, when it is writ so large that you may consider the alternative – to cease to exist, possibly the only true choice we have in life; to continue with life, or to end it?

When I lost Pauline I had nothing to live for. I didn't want to have anything to live for. Gordon was right to phone me every night, because he was concerned about me, as were all the family, and justifiably so, because I did think of an early 'checkout.' I was sustaining myself on cliches for months; hardly a lifeline. I even went online to look for ways of ending it. (Can you really be thinking seriously of suicide if you look online for ways of doing it?) That move brought the first turn around, I think. When I read the comments of some of the 'characters' telling me that I would burn in the hottest fires of Hell, for all eternity, for just thinking about it, I was forced to laugh. I thought, 'too late my friend, I have already committed myself to that fate for having carnal thoughts about Bridget O'Reilly, when I was nine.'

Why the Hell is life so unfair?

I always had a great love for life, since I had come to the realisation that it was all I was ever going to get. I also know that I am cursed to live until I am 108. I do not see existence as purposeless; I just feel that we must set our own purposes for living. As absurd and pointless as life is, I still feel the need to bring some purpose to my being, as pointless as that may seem.

What has been said, by everyone around me, is absolutely true. We may only have had two years, but Pauline was blissfully happy for those two years, and so was I. Living without her is extremely difficult, and it will never get easy, but I desperately hope that it may become tolerable.

When we had first come together again, so many people had said, 'it was meant to be,' as if our lives really are predestined in that precise manner, but when Pauline died; death being the only thing that is really predestined in life, from the moment we are born, no-one said 'it was meant to be.' The happiness of our being together again, after fifty seven years, prompted people to want it to be 'meant,' because that is how they wanted things to happen in their lives. Love and happiness is what all of us want to see in our years ahead, and thinking of the really inevitable is not a part of that dream.

Back in 'that June,' Pauline had said that she only had about two years to live. Neither of us believed it, then, but I remember the tears I shed when she said it. I couldn't bear to think of it being true then, and I have difficulty in believing it to be true now.

The great mistake we made was to repeat the errors of 1954. We had been so consumed with happiness that we felt in control of our own destinies. We had believed that the power of our love made us immortal.

It is some consolation that we had that two and a half wonderful years together. We had given ourselves a future. It wasn't to be for very long, but our horizon stretched distantly before us, and I think it is better to depart this world in the middle of a future, rather than at the end of the past.

Before I go, I must tell you that my poor old companion, Maisie, was to last for just two months beyond Pauline. We had become very firm friends.

SONNETS
FOR PAULINE

BUTTERFLY

October 2012

As the warmth of the sun glows
To a new day a new life
Opens a thing of infinite beauty
Unfolds from its varnished casket
And relishes its freedom to fly
A tissue-delicate life
Not the first birth for
It has been before another
Life so wondrously different a different
Beauty in a different form but with
A heart so cruelly stilled like
Death but not dead only sleeping
Nothing ever dies for life
Like love is eternal.

PARTING

January 2013

A deep rosy glow fills
Our Spanish sky and birds
Like black teardrops falling
From the face of the globe
Reflect the tears that we feel
Through the silent clasp of our hands
We are joined inseparably across
A million miles of separation
Apart but not torn apart
Like once we were
The setting sun is rising
On another day in another place
Our sun can never go down beyond the vision
That is our hearts' horizon.

ONE YEAR

October 2013

Busy old year brings us back
To where we started but
Not where we began
In that Spring of our tender years
When the seasons of our life were
Rooted deep and fateful words indelibly written
Each diurnal now from dawn to dark
A new page of our story
Each season a chapter of sunlight
Through rain and snow flowers and falling leaves
We are a story that will never end
Told and retold for all eternity
A circle of life and love
A garland of two loves entwined.

INTO THE DARKNESS

November 2014

That infinite blackness in the dead of that darkest night
Holds no fear for me nor will
The intense heat of the brightest day
Lay me low
It is that place where
The sinking day meets
That black shroud of the night
That no-mans-land of dread
Where fear steals my soul
And a fierce iciness grips my heart
We have stood in that terrible twilight
Naked and alone together
Between the light and the dark
Twixt the quick and the dead.